Rocks & Sce
of the
Peak Distr...

Trevor D. Ford

Rocks & Scenery
of the
Peak District

Trevor D. Ford

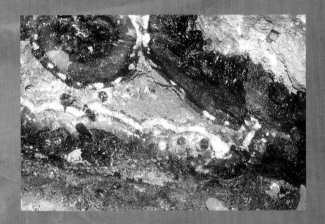

Landmark Publishing

Published by

Ashbourne Hall, Cokayne Ave
Ashbourne, Derbyshire DE6 1EJ England
Tel: (01335) 347349 Fax: (01335) 347303
e-mail: landmark@clara.net
web site: www.landmarkpublishing.co.uk

British Library Cataloguing in Publication Data

ISBN 1-84306-026-4

Printed by Gutenberg Press Ltd, Malta
Designed by Ashley Emery

Photographs by
Trevor Ford pp3, 6, 14, 22, 23, 31b, 38, 46, 50tm, 51t, 62m, 63, 67t,
68, 74, back cover lower; Paul Deakin pp14t, 15b, 31t, 39
Stephen Hopkins pp26, 27t, 50b, 51b, 55, 58, 62tb, 64, 66t, 67b;
John Hopkins pp2-3, cover background;
Lindsey Porter pp27b, 66m, 66b, 70, 71, back cover upper, front cover;
Ashley Emery pp15t

Front cover: The Winnats Pass at Castleton
Back cover: Treak Cliff Cavern, Castleton; Dovedale
Page 3: A cavity lined with Blue John fluorspar (inset)
Aerial photograph of Cave Dale, Castleton

Contents

Preface

The Peak District has an enthralling story to tell of the evolution of its rocks and landscape. Most of it is within a National Park and several areas are either Nature Reserves or Sites of Special Scientific Interest designated by English Nature. This little book attempts to put the story in layman's language so one does not need to be a professional geologist to understand it all.

The story is in two parts: firstly, the rocks themselves tell of their formation in changing geographies some 300 million years ago; secondly, the present day landscape has been carved into those rocks by a variety of processes, including the glaciers of the Ice Age.

My story is the result of over fifty years experience in the Peak District, and many earlier publications, mostly now out of print, have contributed the diagrams and illustrations herein. The author's colleagues and the various publishers are thanked for their co-operation in allowing their re-use. A reading list of the more technical publications is given at the end. These should all be available through public libraries.

Trevor D.Ford, O.B.E., Ph.D., B.Sc., F.G.S.
Honorary Research Fellow,
Geology Department,
University of Leicester,
Leicester LE1 7RH

April 2002

USEFUL MAPS
ORDNANCE SURVEY Landranger 1:50000 maps:
Sheet 110 Sheffield & Huddersfield
Sheet 119 Buxton, Matlock and Dovedale

O.S. 1:25000 map for the White Peak.

BRITISH GEOLOGICAL SURVEY 1:50000 geological maps:
Sheet 99 Chapel-en-le-Frith
Sheet 100 Sheffield
Sheet 111 Buxton, Leek & Bakewell
Sheet 112 Chesterfield & Matlock
Sheet 124 Ashbourne & Cheadle
Sheet 125 Derby
Most of the White Peak is available on 1:25000 geological maps

Introduction

Dark Peak and White Peak

The Dark and White parts of the Peak District are the contrasting parts of the southern end of the Pennine Hills, the backbone of England. To the north the Dark Peak is composed of a series of sandstones and shales, generally brown or black, whilst the White Peak is mainly limestones, of light grey tones. Consideration of this geological contrast is essential for any attempt to understand the scenery. One does not have to be a professional geologist to comprehend the story: indeed it is better to imagine oneself as a detective examining clues in the rocks and deducing the evolutionary story of the landscape and its rocky foundations.

So, in this little book, I shall hope to open your mind to seeing the landscape through the detective eyes of a geologist. Inevitably some jargon must creep in but I shall try to keep it to a minimum and explain the terms as they crop up. But, first we must take a broad look at the Peak District's physical features.

The **Dark Peak** is characterized by moorlands, with the dark shades of heather blending with the brown sandstones and black shales of the Millstone Grit. The wide expanses of moorland are separated by deeply incised valleys margined by prominent escarpments - the edges beloved by rock climbers. The valleys are marked by farmland, mostly pastures, with villages built of weathered sandstones, often midst stands of conifer trees. Some valleys also contain sheets of impounded water in reservoirs. The Millstone Grit moorlands and edges form a horse-shoe frame to the White Peak - a rough frame to a mellow core. The prongs of the horse-shoe include the Staffordshire Moorlands to the west, with deeply indented valley and ridge topography, whilst to the east are the East Moors adjacent to Chesterfield and Sheffield.

The **White Peak** comprises many varieties of limestone, in shades of light and dark grey, mostly covered by thin soils bearing grasslands. Its open vistas are broken by numerous stone walls, interspersed with quarries old and new. Deep narrow dales break the limestone plateau into blocks, with deciduous trees on the dale sides. Farmhouses, cottages and villages are of light grey limestone, blending into the landscape. Many of the dales are dry, that is they have no streams, and villages tend to be sited where springs rise from underground drainage, often from caves. The limestone plateau is further diversified by outcrops of "toadstone", basalt lavas which erupted on to the sea floor, by the many traces of ancient lead mine workings, by silica-sand pockets and by caves.

Together, the Dark and White Peaks were designated as Britain's first National Park in 1951 in view of the scenic and cultural heritage therein. The **Peak District National Park** lies within an hour or so's drive of half England's population so that such an area also serves as recreational "lungs". Many areas of the Peak have long been recognized as of scenic value and some have been acquired by the National Trust and other organizations. Some areas, particularly in the White Peak, are recognized as requiring conservation and have been designated as National Nature Reserves or as SSSIs (Sites of Special Scientific Interest) by English Nature (and its predecessor The Nature Conservancy). Many archaeological sites and historic buildings have been listed under Ancient Monument legislation.

The logical way to study the evolution of the Peak District is to look at the rocks themselves first, to see what they tell us about their origin, about the geography of the ancient times when they were formed, about what has happened to them since, and only then to look at the processes and sequence of events which have moulded the rocks into today's landscape.

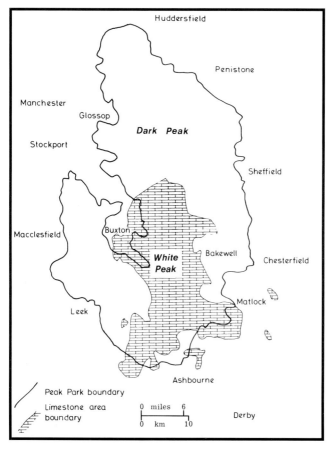

Sketch map of the Dark and White Peak and the National Park.

1
The Limestones
of the White Peak

Limestones form the core of the Peak District and they are the oldest visible rocks. They lie on a deeply buried and hidden basement of much older slaty and volcanic rocks similar to those of Wales, known only from two deep boreholes. With a surface of an unknown topography, the basement was submerged by the encroachment of the sea in early Carboniferous times, some 350 million years ago. The Peak District was not in today's cool temperate climate at that time; instead it was tropical, with the limestones being composed of fragments of shells and corals together with abundant remains of crinoids. Though the latter look like plants, they are in fact animals related to starfish and sea-urchins. Many species of these groups are present as fossils in the limestones. Have a close look at any crag, cliff or wall. Some were fossilized complete, but many others were broken to bits by the action of the waves. They were rolled about and smashed to pieces by tides and currents on a shallow sea floor. Fragments of lime-secreting sea-weeds confirm that the sea was shallow enough in places for sunlight to penetrate and effect photosynthesis. The fossilized marine organisms demonstrate that Britain's environment was tropical in early Carboniferous times. Corals were not as abundant as on modern reefs and so the Peak District reefs are less like the atolls of today.

The orientation of the traces of magnetic minerals in our rocks can be measured and they show that Britain lay just south of the Equator at the beginning of Carboniferous times. As part of the Earth's system of moving continental plates, Britain has been drifting slowly northwards ever since, and after 300 million years Britain is more than halfway to the North Pole.

Thus, when we look at the limestones, we must forget Britain's geography as it is today and picture ourselves standing (or swimming) in a clear, shallow, warm, tropical sea, perhaps comparable with the Australian Great Barrier Reef or Pacific atolls today.

How do we know that it was more than 300 million years ago? Peak District rocks, and many others of comparable nature elsewhere, contain minute quantities of radioactive elements such as uranium. If these elements are extracted the proportions of uranium and its radio-active decay products (known as daughters) can be measured in a mass spectrometer. As we know the rate of decay, we can then calculate the age of the rocks concerned. The limestones of the Peak District accumulated from around 350 to 310 million years ago, a period, of some 40 million years. Such ages may seem astronomical but the limestones are less than a tenth of the age of the Earth and much

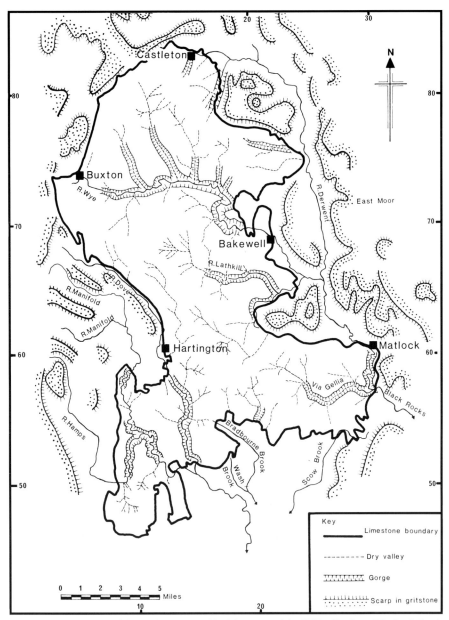

Simplified sketch map of the main topographical features of the White Peak and its Dark Peak frame of gritstone edges.

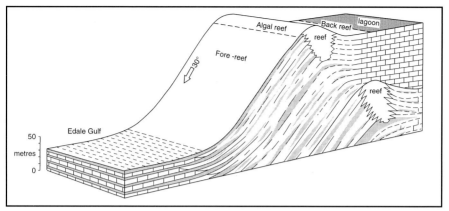

Diagram of the relationship of lagoon, reef, fore-reef and gulf limestones in Carboniferous times. Based on sections in the Winnats Pass, Castleton.

has happened since then. The Peak District was part of a northwest European plate then, moving slowly northwards. The rate of movement of the Earth's continental "plates" is slow but over millions of years the cumulative effect is enormous. Today, with the aid of satellite systems, we know that Europe and America are moving apart at about 5 cm per year, roughly the rate at which our fingernails grow!

With 40 million years for the accumulation of our limestones, which have a maximum thickness of some 2000 metres, we can calculate that the average rate of accumulation of shell, coral and crinoid debris was less than a centimetre per century but that is enough to build a substantial mass of limestone.

Detailed examination of the limestone beds shows that they vary considerably. In some beds complete shells of brachiopods lie in bands and these are separated by layers with their fragments broken up so finely that they are visible only under a microscope. Similarly fossil corals only occur in isolated beds, whilst others have been smashed to bits by the waves. Broken shell limestones are known as bioclastic (i.e. biological material broken by physical actions). Such bioclastic limestones occupy much of the central area of the White Peak, where regular limestone strata can be seen along the dale sides. Good examples are in Monsal, Millers and Lathkill Dales. In the last-named dale, the long-disused Ricklow Quarry, about 1.5 km east of Monyash, has beds of limestone packed with the fossil brachiopod *Gigantoproductus*, interlayered with beds made of masses of crinoid stem fragments: together these were once exploited as "figured marble", and polished slabs show the details in fireplaces, windowsills, washstand tops, flooring and monuments. Good examples are in Chatsworth House, whilst the new Coventry Cathedral and both flooring and windowsills of Heathrow's terminals were made from the equivalent "marble" obtained near Wirksworth.

But, to return to the Carboniferous period, around the edges of the White Peak are a scatter of mound-like masses of fine-grained limestone. Commonly called reefs, they are more properly referred to as mud-mounds or build-ups: they have also been

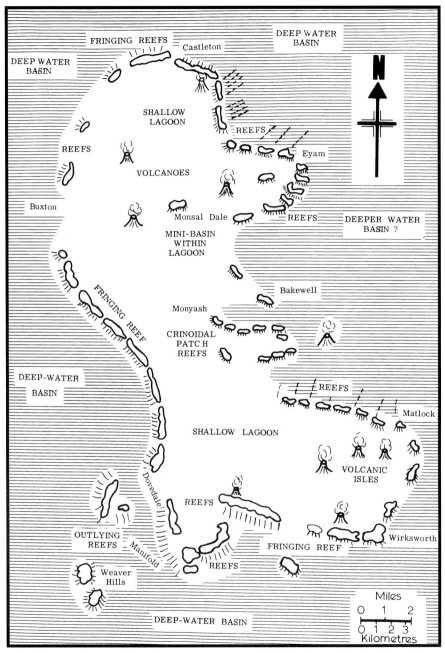

A simplified sketch map of the palaeogeography of the White Peak in early Carboniferous times. It should be noted that the features shown are not all of exactly the same geological age.

called knolls or bioherms. Such reefs are to be found around Castleton, Bradwell, Eyam, Monyash, Matlock and Wirksworth. They are not all of the same age so that the reconstruction of the Peak atoll is a composite of reefs of slightly different ages.

Reef limestones consist of fine-grained lime-mud formed by microscopic algae. These are filamentous sea-weeds which deposit calcite in their cell walls during growth on the sea bed, and which also act as sticky trapping devices for lime-mud washing around on the sea-floor. Together these processes mean that the mud-mounds grew above the general level of their surroundings. A classic example is to be seen in section in the cliff of High Tor overlooking the Derwent Gorge at Matlock. Others are well-exposed in the old quarries forming part of the National Stone Centre at Wirksworth. A mass of mud-mounds forms Treak Cliff at Castleton, and sections of them can be seen in the nearby Winnats Pass and Cavedale: Peveril Castle is built on top of a pile of reefs. The prominent Chrome and Parkhouse Hills in Upper Dovedale are further examples. Sheltering among the algal filament mats particularly around the flanks of the mud-mounds were abundant shells and their fossils are common wherever the mud-mounds outcrop, as seen in Ricklow Quarry and in the reef quarry of the National Stone Centre. The fossils include brachiopods, molluscs, small corals, bryozoans, trilobites (rare) and goniatites (the latter are similar to the present-day Nautilus). Occasional fish teeth and scales are found in some inter-reef limestones. The reefs of Castleton and Upper Dovedale are asymmetrical, that is, they were built on the edge of the limestone massif, with flat-lying **lagoonal limestones** on one side, and a steep **fore-reef** slope into deeper water on the other. The outer slopes of Treak Cliff and Chrome Hill are fine fore-reefs. Many shells and their fragments accumulated on the fore-reef slopes and they are fine fossil-hunting ground.

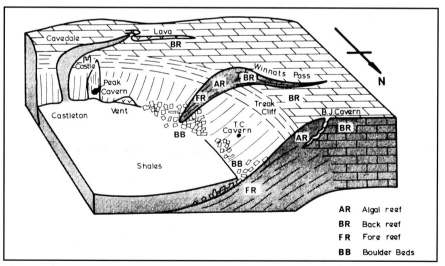

Block diagram to show the relationship of the reef margins of the White Peak around Castleton. The channels of the Winnats Pass and Cavedale were cut through the reefs later.

Contorted strata on a copper vein, Royledge Mine near Ecton. Just to the left of this photo, the beds become horizontal

Oily and rubbery bitumens seeping out of the limestone at Windy Knoll, near Castleton

Nodules and bands of chert in the limestone of Steeplehouse Quarry, Wirksworth

Middle Peak
Quarry,
Wirksworth

A combination of
thin and thick
beds, Royledge
Mine Adit.
The miners
associated
copper deposits
with thick beds

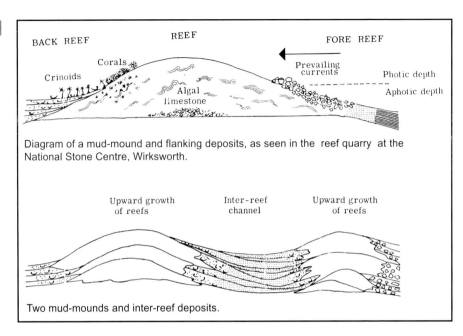

Diagram of a mud-mound and flanking deposits, as seen in the reef quarry at the National Stone Centre, Wirksworth.

Two mud-mounds and inter-reef deposits.

In lower Dovedale and the adjacent Manifold Valley are a subtly different type of **mud-mounds**. They developed in deeper water which lacked photosynthetic algae, but the lace-like fans of bryozoans trapped the finer lime sediment to form mounds on the lower slopes of a ramp-like configuration of the sea-floor. Examples are Beeston Tor in the Manifold Valley, and Raven Tor and the Doveholes Crag in Dovedale. Thorpe Cloud and Bunster at the southern end of Dovedale are an intermediate type where the deep-water mud-mounds grew sufficiently close to sea-level for algae and shells to colonize their crests. Further to the southwest are more shelly mounds in the Weaver Hills.

Taking the core area of the White Peak as largely shallow-water bioclastic limestones with an intermittent frame of reef-like mud-mounds means that the whole area is broadly comparable to a Pacific atoll today. Indeed, with dimensions of some 50 km north-south and 20 km east-west, the White Peak is of comparable size to Bikini Atoll. All that is missing is a scenario of palm trees and girls in grass skirts! However, Derbyshire was an incomplete atoll with several large gaps in its ring of reefs, and the reef margin is not of the same age all the way round the White Peak. A gap in the ring of reefs is marked by a ramp and its deep-water mounds in the Dovedale-Manifold area. Offshore, beyond the mound complexes, lay deeper water and thin beds of dark muddy limestone accumulated in basins there. These can be seen along much of the Manifold valley, particularly at Apes Tor. A smaller deep-water basin lay around Monsal Dale and Ashford-in-the Water and the thin dark limestones there can be polished to yield Black Marble. To the southwest, the Weaver Hills show shallow water limestones and a few reefs and another massif may be hidden beneath younger strata still further southwest.

The reef margin of the White Peak was also diversified by channels cut by tides and currents sweeping in and out of the lagoon. The Winnats Pass at Castleton appears to been initiated as a channel. Another is between Thorpe Cloud and Bunster in Lower Dovedale. At the end of the limestone period, uplift caused parts of the reef margin, particularly around Castleton, to be eroded and boulder beds accumulated at the foot of the fore-reef slopes.

Apart from the reefs, which hardened into solid limestone very soon after they were formed, most of the White Peak atoll floor was loose lime-sediment and its transformation into limestone is the process known as lithification or diagenesis. When a sediment is buried beneath later layers a small amount of sea-water is trapped in the pores between grains. With the pressures of burial this becomes chemically active. The shell fragments have various compositions, calcite or aragonite, and trace elements are present, to which are added the decaying soft parts of the animals. The trapped waters become acidic here and alkaline there and as pressures move the fluids around they react with each other. Susceptible aragonite particles are dissolved and may be precipitated elsewhere as calcite forming cement holding the grains together.

The soft parts of the fossilized organisms rotted in the pores of the lime-sediment to yield hydrocarbons - the starting point for oil generation. Some limestone blocks smell distinctly oily when freshly broken, but unfortunately there was never enough hydrocarbon to make an oilfield. Occasionally bitumens accumulated in voids such as hollow fossil shells. An unusual example of a hydrocarbon accumulation is at Windy Knoll above Castleton, where various oily and rubbery bitumens ooze out of the rock.

From time to time the White Peak's lagoon was filled with sediments, and its reefs grew to sea-level so that all or part of the region was dry land, like the Bahamas Islands today. Soils developed on the limestone islands and vegetation took root. Traces of palaeosols are only to be found by microscopic study, but they are more common than often appreciated. Occasional eruptions of volcanic ash filled the lagoon up to sea level and plants took root on the low-lying islands giving another variety of ancient soil.

Chert nodules characterize many limestones. These formed because the lagoonal sea-water contained a small proportion of microscopic organisms with siliceous skeletons. When they died and decayed their silica was dispersed and being soluble in alkaline waters, it moved around until it met acid conditions where it was precipitated as nodules of chert. These hard nodules stand out on weathered surfaces, rather like flint nodules in the chalk cliffs of Dover.

Dolomite or partly dolomitized limestone results from the introduction of magnesium into the calcium carbonate molecule as the double carbonate of calcium and magnesium. Several square kilometres of the southern end of the White Peak has had magnesium introduced into the lime molecules and the resultant rock is largely made of dolomite. Its distinctive grey-brown, dun, colour is well seen in Harborough and Rainster Rocks near Brassington, much favoured by rock-climbers. The source of the magnesium and the rather limited area which has been dolomitized are uncertain but it may be an early phase of the process of forming mineral veins (see below).

Diagenesis destroys some fossils but others remain untouched. If you look at them, a magnifying glass will reveal exquisite detail of long-dead shells preserved through

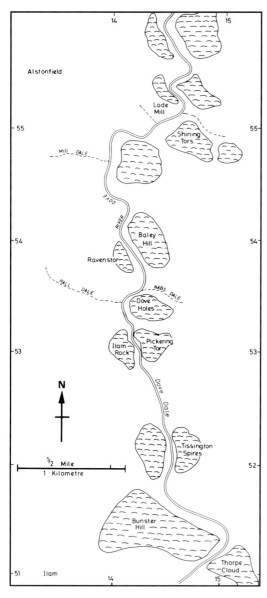

Sketch map of Lower Dovedale with the river meandering between masses of mud-mound limestone.

the millions of years. Occasionally shades of grey reflect the original colouring of the shells. But fossils should not be collected simply to be stuck in a box like stamps in an album - they are the clues on which geologists build up their picture of ancient lagoons and reefs. Leave collecting to the professional geologist. This book does not list collecting localities as so many have been ruined by indiscriminate hammering.

Our White Peak lagoon did not maintain the same geography throughout the 40 million years of early Carboniferous times. The sketch map is a composite of the palaeo-geography over some million of years. To add to the story of the White Peak, the Earth's crust is in a constant state of movement, and the stresses caused folding and faulting which have moved the beds away from their original attitude. Stresses within the Earth also caused parts of its interior to be so heated that they burst forth to build up volcanoes. These matters of stress and eruption are described later.

Thus, the White Peak's limestones illustrate a wide variety of phenonema, from reefs and mounds to lagoons, with their associated fossils. Processes of converting lime-sediment to rock are well-displayed, with the by-products of chert nodules, dolomite and bitumens. With folds, faults, volcanic rocks and mineral veins thrown in, the White Peak is a fascinating glimpse of Britain's past as can be seen from the following chapters.

2

Toadstones or Volcanic
Lavas and Ash Falls

As detectives reading the clues of the rocks, we have deduced a picture of an atoll in Carboniferous times, on or close to the Equator, with the Earth's crust showing signs of instability. From time to time, lava burst forth from submarine volcanic vents onto the floor of the lagoon, as it does on a few Pacific islands today. The vents were generally small and little evidence has been found to indicate that there were giant volcanic peaks like those of Vesuvius or Hawaii today. But volcanoes there were, and their lava was fluid basalt that flowed far across the lagoon floor. Each flow was probably erupted from its vent in a few hours or days, but repeated eruptions over a period meant that in places the basalt pile may have been a hundred metres or more in thickness. Some of the lavas were very gassy and the frozen bubbles are now seen as vesicles, little cavities in rather porous basalt. Toadstone proper results when these are filled in with chlorite and other greeny-black minerals to give the spotted colouring of a toad. The thicker lava flows cooled more slowly and occasionally developed hexagonal columns. Examples can be seen in Cavedale and in Calton Hill quarry.

In contrast to lava some eruptions resulted in clouds of volcanic dust or ash spewed out to form beds known as tuff, either interlayered with the basalt or sometimes separate. Thin layers of volcanic dust gave what are known as wayboards between beds of limestone. These are usually not more than a few centimetres thick but may reach a metre or so. Root-like markings suggest that land plants sometimes colonized the banks of ash and dust. After each eruption was over, marine life re-colonized the lagoon floor and more beds of limestone covered the lava and ash sheets.

The Peak District lavas have a mineral composition known as basalt and compare with many other basalts around the World. Iceland and the Hawaiian Islands are made of such lavas. The dark greeny-blue rocks contrast with the light grey limestones. Basalt tends to weather to a dappled greeny-brown but it is often hidden from view beneath soil and vegetation. Good examples are in Millers Dale, capping the old quarries near the former railway station, at the foot of Raven Tor and in the old railway cuttings. There are other outcrops of basalt in Tideswell Dale, Cressbrook Dale and around the foot of Taddington Dale. The nearby Black Rock Corner on the A6 about 1.5 km west of Ashford-in-the-Water is a fine example. Another well-known example is in Cavedale, near Castleton.

Volcanic vents are the feeder conduits by which the lavas reached the surface. They are marked by small irregular outcrops of basalt, often with the lava broken into fragments (or brecciated, as geologists say). Examples are near the Speedwell Mine at

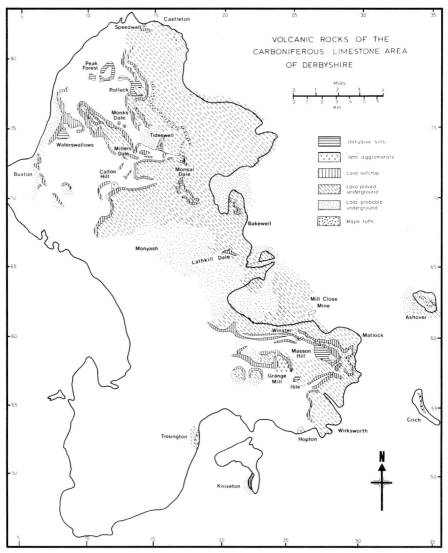

Sketch map of the distribution of toadstones (lavas and ashes) both as surface outcrops and projected underground extent.

Castleton, in Monks Dale, at Calton Hill near Taddington and at Ashover. Masson Hill, above Matlock, is partly cored by a vent and two main lava flows extend from it. One may be seen in the entrance passage to Rutland Cavern.

Sheets of basaltic magma which did not reach the surface were sometimes emplaced within the limestone strata. Such sheets are known as sills, and good examples occur at Peak Forest, Waterswallows near Buxton, Ible in the Via Gellia, and around the summit of Masson Hill. In sills the magma cooled more slowly and the individual crystals are larger, giving the igneous rock type known as dolerite. A few vertical sheets of dolerite known as dykes are also present in the Peak District, the best known being in Peak Dale.

The basaltic lavas and ashes of the White Peak have long been known as **toadstones**. There are several possible explanations for this quaint name. As noted above, one is that the mottled green and brown colouring is like the back of a toad. Another is that German miners working in the lead mines realized that in sinking their shafts, they would lose the lead vein on striking the basalt, so they called it in German todt-stein meaning dead or unproductive rock, and the Derbyshire mispronunciation soon made that into toadstone. Finally, Derbyshire dialect commonly uses the term **t'owd** (meaning "the old...") as an expression of disgust, so a lead miner reaching lava in his mine might say **"t'owd stone again"**.

Basaltic rocks are usually in demand for aggregate in road-building and there were once a dozen quarries working them in the White Peak, but only one is left - Waterswallows Quarry near Buxton. At Calton Hill, near Taddington, the quarry has been partly filled with waste, and the large waste heaps have been landscaped and returned to agriculture, but several small quarry faces have been left with these interesting rocks exposed for posterity. One section is particularly interesting as the eruptions brought up nodules of the green mineral olivine from deep in the Earth's crust.

The basalt and tuff layers are almost impervious and affect the movement of underground water by constraining it within the limestones in contact with toadstones. Several caves originated on the limestone/toadstone contact and some mineral deposits were formed from fluids ponded against toadstones. Much of the eastern part of the White Peak has toadstones known below the surface but which have no outcrops.

Basalt columns resulting from slow cooling of a massive flow. Calton Hill quarry, Taddington

Massive lagoonal limestone resting on a basalt lava flow. Ravenstor, Millers Dale

A wayboard of volcanic dust between limestone beds. Masson Hill, Matlock

Black Rock Corner near Ashford-in-the-Water, with a thick lava outcropping at the right

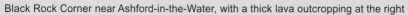

3

The Millstone Grit

Take a walk up Grindsbrook along the start of the Pennine Way or up any of the other cloughs in Edale, and look into the stream banks from time to time. Apart from a scatter of fallen sandstone blocks you will see that the lower slopes of Kinder Scout are characterized by blue-black shales, and as you climb higher you cross on to sandstones. These are rather thin-bedded at first but as you reach the edge of the Kinder Scout plateau massive gritstones are present. The latter are 30 m thick or more. A similar series of strata may be traversed by climbing Mam Tor from near Odin Mine, west of Castleton, except that it does not reach the massive sandstones and most of the hill is in the Mam Tor Sandstones. The same sequence of Millstone Grit strata may be crossed by hiking from the limestone margin west of Buxton up to Axe Edge, or by walking from the High Peak Trail up past Black Rocks to Barrel Edge, northeast of Wirksworth. The sandstones are obvious but the shales are only seen in mine waste heaps.

Together these traverses illustrate the contrast of White and Dark Peaks. They show how the limestone plateau of the former is surrounded by the shales and sandstones of the Millstone Grit. The sequence of shale, thin sandstones (called flagstones when they can be split into thin slabs) and massive sandstones (usually called gritstones in the Pennines) is the product of a great delta being built out by a river flowing into the Pennine sedimentary basin. By observations throughout the Pennines the ancient geography of the rivers and delta system can be reconstructed to a fair degree of accuracy. The river-delta system arose from the erosion of a mountain chain on the site of the present Scottish Highlands discharging its waste products into the Pennine basin. Comparable deltas are forming today at the mouths of the Mississippi, Nile, Niger, Ganges and many other rivers. So, if you had been standing where the Kinder Scout plateau is now during Carboniferous times, some 300 million years ago, you would have been on a swampy delta-flat with sluggish distributary streams carrying loads of mud, silt and sand out towards the sea. Thick vegetation, trees, ferns and mosses, clothed the banks and their fossil remains occasionally accumulated as peat which time and pressure converted to coal seams. Most of the coals are but a few centimetres thick but a few thicker seams have been mined as on Goldsitch Moss west of Buxton and near Ringinglow, on the edge of the moors above Sheffield. Fossil plants can also be found in some of the sandstones, for example in the thin sandstones exposed in the face of Mam Tor.

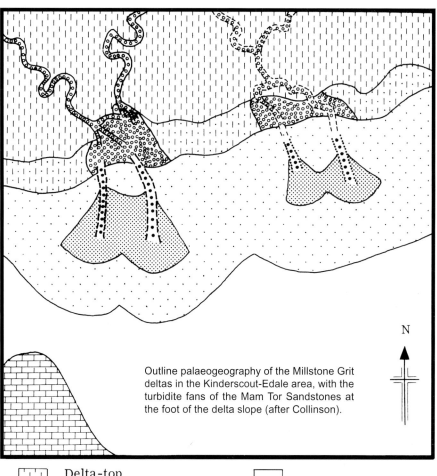

Outline palaeogeography of the Millstone Grit deltas in the Kinderscout-Edale area, with the turbidite fans of the Mam Tor Sandstones at the foot of the delta slope (after Collinson).

N

	Delta-top interdistributary		Mud deposition
	Prograding slope		Limestone
	The bottom of the delta-slope with muddy slurry (turbidite)		Migrating fluviatile channel
	Distal turbidite apron		Deep turbidite channel
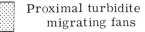	Proximal turbidite migrating fans		

Two views from Curbar Edge looking towards Froggatt Edge

Millstones cut from the sandstone of Stanage Edge

The outcropping gritstones on the western side of the Peak.
Ramshaw Rocks on The Roaches

Don't go too close to the face of Mam Tor or it may live up to its alternative name of Shivering Mountain and loose lumps may fall off - onto your head.

Each delta is complex: meandering distributaries spread from the feeder river across the delta-top. The load of sand, silt and mud tends to be deposited where deeper water is met and, if the pile of sediment is shaken, perhaps by an earthquake, it may sweep down the slope as a "soup" of sediment and water. The sediment is then deposited as the velocity is reduced at the foot of the slope and it yields a turbidite fan. Sand settles first, followed by mud. In Mam Tor around a hundred repetitions of sand and mudstone make up the landslip scar. Mud alone is swept out into the deep-water basin and settles there to be compressed to shale later. Such shales floor Edale and form the lowest stratal unit of the Millstone Grit, in contact with the limestone. These components of a delta may be recognized in many parts of the Dark Peak, but the Mam Tor ridge and the slopes of Kinder Scout provide the best examples.

The delta built out until it impinged on the limestone reefs of Treak Cliff and later it extended to cover the whole of the limestone massif. The escarpments in the horse-shoe frame round its edges are the eroded remnants of a sequence of Millstone Grit deltas. As each delta built out into the sea the latter was more or less filled with sediment, but intermittent renewals of Earth movements caused repeated subsidences, and each time the process of building out a delta started again. So the Millstone Grit Series as a whole consists of several repetitions of the sequence shale-siltstone-sandstone, representing a series of deltas piled one on top of the other. All have been breached by erosion so that the eroded ends of the thick massive sandstones now form a series of escarpments known as Edges. Stanage Edge, Derwent Edge, Millstone Edge, Higgar Tor and Burbage Rocks, Curbar Edge, Baslow Edge, Barrel Edge etc overlook the Derwent Valley. To the west, Axe Edge, Ramshaw Rocks, the Roaches and Hen Cloud are the eroded remnants of the same deltas as those on the east of the Peak District. All show the inclined foreset bedding typical of the structure of deltas in their cliff faces, and the foreset bedding is oriented with the river flow from northeast to southwest, confirming the deduction of a massive river system draining the Scottish Highlands.

The coarse sandstones are very abrasive and our prehistoric ancestors used slabs to grind their corn into flour. This unfortunately added sand to their bread and their teeth wore down rapidly. Later, blocks and slabs were quarried as building stone - many Peak District villages have houses built of them, and the thin sandstones were used as paving flagstones or, if thin enough, as roofing slates. Even in the limestone country lintels and doorposts are made of Millstone Grit blocks. Stately homes such as Chatsworth House are made of Millstone Grit sandstones. By Mediaeval times grinding wheels were cut out for the Sheffield tool and cutlery industry, and they are mentioned indirectly in one of Chaucer's Canterbury tales, wherein the Reeve's Sheffield Thwytle (a sort of knife) was sharpened on a sandstone wheel. Unsold and unfinished millstone wheels are common lying around the old quarries at Millstone Edge above Hathersage. The trade was killed off when synthetic abrasives such as carborundum were introduced early in the 20th century. Today, the Edges provide great sport for rock climbers.

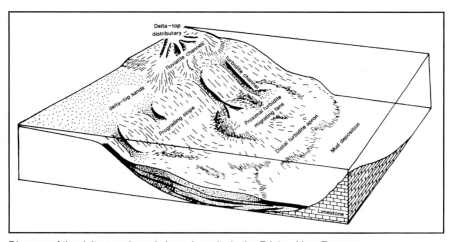

Diagram of the delta margin and slope deposits in the Edale - Mam Tor area.

The contrast of geographies of the limestone lagoon with spluttering volcanoes against the deltas of the Millstone Grit is dramatic. It gives us the distinctive White and Dark Peaks. Such contrast requires explanation. It lies in the simple fact that the Earth's crust is never stable; parts are moving relative to sea level and to each other all the time, sometimes slowly, sometimes fast. Slow movements may raise or depress blocks of the Earth's crust. In mid-Carboniferous times, some 300 million years ago, major movements took place: the limestone massif was depressed too far below sea level for the many organisms to survive so that limestone sedimentation ceased. At about the same time, the Scottish Highlands and their ancestor ranges were uplifted. Erosion of this much larger mountain range than is present today yielded the vast quantities of sediment now known as the Millstone Grit.

The uplift, erosion, transport of sediment by rivers continued into latest Carboniferous times and gave us the **Coal Measures** of the coalfields lying either side of the Peak District. Longer periods of quiescence allowed more decaying vegetation to accumulate as massive beds of peat. Later compression of the peats yielded the many coal seams. The coalfields are not part of the Peak District so that story must be told elsewhere, but, like the Millstone Grit deltas, the Coal Measures once extended right across the White Peak. Relics are preserved only in a small part of the Goyt Valley, northwest of Buxton, near Ringinglow, west of Sheffield, on the eastern limits of the East Moors near Chesterfield and on the eastern flanks of the Ashover and Crich folds.

Together Millstone Grit and Coal Measures total more than 2 km in thickness, so the limestone was once buried by that amount.

4

Structures
Folds and Faults

It may come as a surprise to many readers to think of rocks being folded, but without folds which lift up strata and expose them to erosion, then our whole landscape would be a flat sheet of the last sediments derived from the last mountains.

Folds come in all sizes, from small ones a few metres across, as can be seen at Apes Tor, near Ecton, Staffordshire. Here thin beds of limestone with shale partings have folded with an amplitude of perhaps 5 metres and a wave-length of not much more. Both anticlines (upfolds) and synclines (downfolds) are present and in some cases the beds have been brought to a near vertical position. Along the disused Newton Grange railway cutting on the Tissington Trail is a medium scale fold, perhaps 10 m amplitude and 50 m across. Edale marks a larger anticline as the sandstones are gently inclined outwards on both sides: they have been eroded away to expose shales in the core. Ashover is a similar anticline but the higher beds of limestone have been breached by erosion to expose volcanic rocks in the core. The nearby Crich Hill, with its memorial tower on the summit overlooking the Tramway Museum, is another upfold, where the limestones beds gently arch along more than a kilometre of the cliff face. Masson Hill at Matlock is a more complex anticline with both limestones and toadstone sheets gently arched over a volcanic vent. The fold exceeds two kilometres in width. The cliffs of High Tor across the Derwent show the trend of beds rising southwards from Matlock to a peak in High Tor itself and then plunging steeply down again near Matlock Bath Station. Steeple Grange village on Bole Hill lies on the crest of an anticline between Cromford and Wirksworth. The limestones of the National Stone Centre lie on its south flank and are inclined southwards whilst the limestones in Dene Quarry to the north are inclined northwards. The Roaches and Ramshaw Rocks are scarps of the same sandstone inclining inwards on either side of a syncline. On a much larger scale, an east-west section across the Peak District is anticlinal with the limestone massif in the core and the Millstone Grit dipping outwards on each flank, with the Coal Measures still further out on each side.

Rocks do not fold instantaneously. The movements are very slow and gentle but, applied over thousands if not millions of years, the overall effect can be dramatic. A Babylonian Canal in the Middle East is in a region which has been folded over the last two millenia - it now holds water only at the two ends as the middle section is some 10m higher. If folding were taking place under our feet we probably would not know it, but given long enough, folding can produce mountain ranges such as the Alps and Himalayas.

Severe folding in Clayton Mine, Ecton, Manifold Valley. The white is whitewash on the wall of the Engine Chamber

A small anticline in the limestones at Apes Tor, Ecton

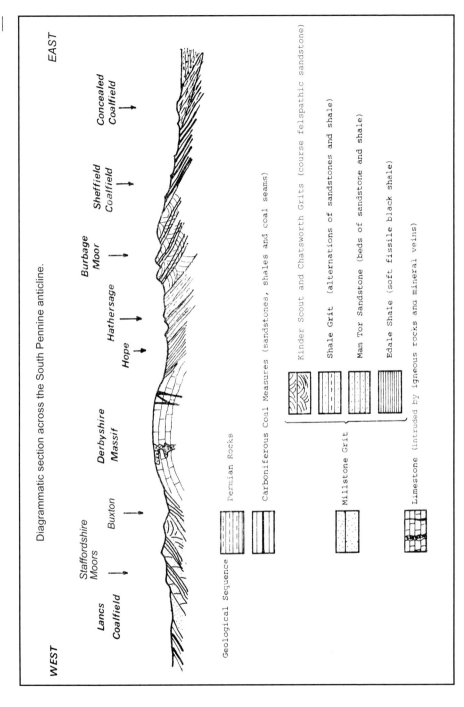

Diagrammatic section across the South Pennine anticline.

WEST

EAST

Lancs Coalfield

Staffordshire Moors

Buxton

Derbyshire Massif

Hope

Hathersage

Burbage Moor

Sheffield Coalfield

Concealed Coalfield

Geological Sequence

Permian Rocks

Carboniferous Coal Measures (sandstones, shales and coal seams)

Kinder Scout and Chatsworth Grits (course felspathic sandstone)

Shale Grit (alternations of sandstones and shale)

Mam Tor Sandstone (beds of sandstone and shale)

Edale Shale (soft fissile black shale)

Millstone Grit

Limestone (intruded by igneous rocks and mineral veins)

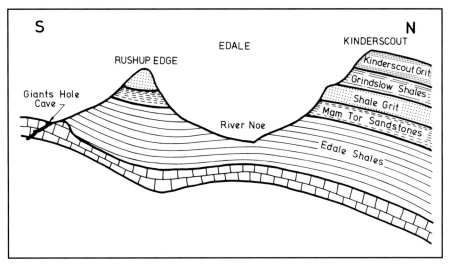

Sketch section across the Edale anticline.

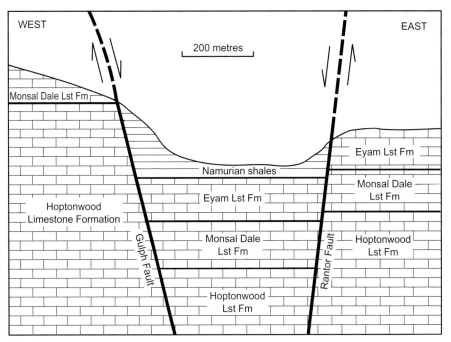

Sketch section across The Gulf at Wirksworth showing the strata dropped down between two faults.

By contrast, faulting is an almost instantaneous process. The stresses of Earth movement build up until the crust snaps under the strain. The lines of fracture are known as faults. The amount of movement at any one time rarely exceeds more than a few metres, but the cumulative effect of many movements on a fault can result in hundreds or even thousands of metres of displacement. Many faults can be mapped by geologists in the Peak District. Perhaps the easiest to understand is The Gulf at Wirksworth: here a block of country about 300 metres wide and a kilometre long has dropped down between two faults, so that the downthrown block is floored by shales, with limestone walls on each side forming a rift valley in miniature. The floor is also broken up by several parallel minor faults which have been mineralized to yield mineral veins. Cross-faulting explains the discontinuous trend of the gritstone escarpments, such as at Curbar Gap.

Many mineral veins are similarly in fault fissures and mining sometimes reveals the nearly horizontal grooves on the walls known as slickensides, where masses of rock have ground against each other. Without folding and faulting we would not have the variety of rocks and scenery shown by the Peak District today.

Both folding and faulting are the visible effects of processes operating on a global scale, with "plates" of the crust moving relative to each other and to the Poles. Towards the end of Carboniferous times these plate movements reached a crescendo and the major earth movements of which the Pennine folds are a part took place. The N.W. European plate, of which Britain is part, has been moving northwards ever since and the Peak District may reach the Pole in about 200 million years.

The Carboniferous period ended about 290 million years ago with most of the folding and faulting dating from that time. Thrown in for good measure was the mineralization responsible for the mineral veins. The subsequent geological history of the South Pennines is not as clear as we would like but scientific studies of strata in surrounding areas such as Lincolnshire and Nottinghamshire on the east and Cheshire and Staffordshire to the west give us some clues. The Peak District was buried in strata of Triassic, Jurassic and Cretaceous ages, from about 200 to 65 million years ago. Estimates vary but most geologists accept that up to 2 km of rocks of these ages once lay across the South Pennines, and thus our limestones were eventually buried to a depth of around 4 km.

Further climaxes in Earth movement took place around 65 and 30 million years ago - the latter saw the rise of the Alps, when the African plate collided with Europe. It was during these episodes that erosion set in across northern England with a vengeance and the cover of younger rocks was totally removed together with the Coal Measures and much of the Millstone Grit, thereby exposing the White Peak limestones with their frame of Dark Peak sandstones.

5

Minerals and Mines

The White Peak has long been noted for its lead mines and the surviving traces form part of our scenic and geological heritage. Industrial archaeologists are fascinated by the old mine buildings, whilst mine enthusiasts and speleologists explore the old mines and their related cave systems. Both old mines and caves are potentially dangerous and should only be entered by experienced people. There are thousands of abandoned mine shafts, some still open and hidden in long grass. Take great care and do not stray from recognized footpaths.

Galena (lead sulphide, PbS) is the principal lead ore. It is no longer mined in its own right, as there is no single deposit large enough for the economics of the big mining companies. But in many mineral deposits the galena is accompanied by fluorspar, baryte and calcite and the lead ore is separated off as a valuable by-product.

Fluorspar (calcium fluoride, CaF_2) is important as it is the raw material for the chemical industry as the source of numerous fluorine compounds. These are used in the fluoridization of toothpaste and water, in the preparation of artificial cryolite as an intermediary in the production of aluminium, in processing uranium ores, in making the non-stick teflon surfaces in saucepans, for special types of ceramics and glasses and as a component of the anaesthetic fluorethane.

Baryte (barium sulphate, $BaSO_4$) is also important economically. It gives weight to glossy paper, acts as substitute for lead in paint, and is used to prepare barium meal for stomach X-rays. Baryte is an important lubricant in oil-well drilling where its weight also helps to keep gas pressures under control. Many thousands of tons have been used in the North Sea oil and gas fields.

Calcite (calcium carbonate, $CaCO_3$) is less valuable to industry but there have been a few mines working calcite only. Transparent calcite was known as Iceland Spar, used in Victorian optical instruments. Most calcite has an opaque whiteness once useful for stucco pebble-dash on houses. It is also used in a special cement base for terrazzo flooring and panels in public buildings. Other uses include the white lines down the middle of roads and the white gravel ornamentation on graves.

Less common are sphalerite (zinc sulphide, ZnS) and chalcopyrite (copper-iron sulphide, Cu,FeS_2). The former was mined for use in brass manufacture whilst the latter was the principal copper ore mined at Ecton in Staffordshire.

These minerals are found in veins in the limestone, known in Derbyshire mining jargon as rakes, scrins, pipes and flats. **Rakes and scrins** are large and small fissure

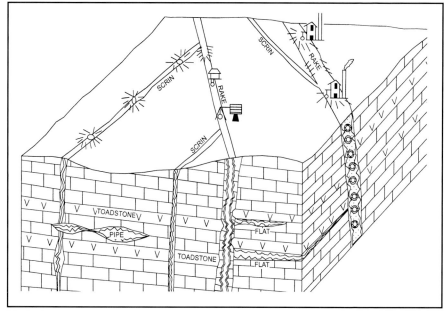

Block diagram to show the relationship of the various types of mineral veins, including rakes, scrins, pipes and flats.

fillings, usually more or less vertical, and they can be followed across country by lines of hollows and mounds marking long abandoned workings. **Pipes and flats** are more irregular; they may occupy ancient cave systems or they may follow single beds of limestone nearly horizontally. Pipes are linings or infillings of ancient caverns and other voids, whilst flats tend to lie along the bedding, often close to thin volcanic layers. A non-traditional type of mineral deposit is **replacements**, where the minerals, mainly fluorspar, replaced the limestone itself molecule by molecule. The surface expression is again mounds and hollows but in irregular clusters not along the lines of fissures. Although they should not be entered, if not overgrown or filled in, the old workings provide interesting exposures of mineral deposition.

Some two thousand named lead veins are known and as each may have several mines, the total number of mines probably exceeds 10,000. The mines were mostly small, often just narrow passages where the whole rake or scrin has been removed. Access was by narrow shafts, sometimes with footholds in the walls or with timbers set across to act as the rungs of a ladder (known as stemples). Larger and deeper mines soon met problems with waterlogged ground and long tunnels (soughs) were driven in from nearby valley sides to drain off the excess water and to lower the water-table. More than a hundred soughs are known, some 5 km or more in length. Their outfalls (tails) discharge millions of gallons of water daily and some is taken into public water supplies. Some mines encountered natural caverns and the miners

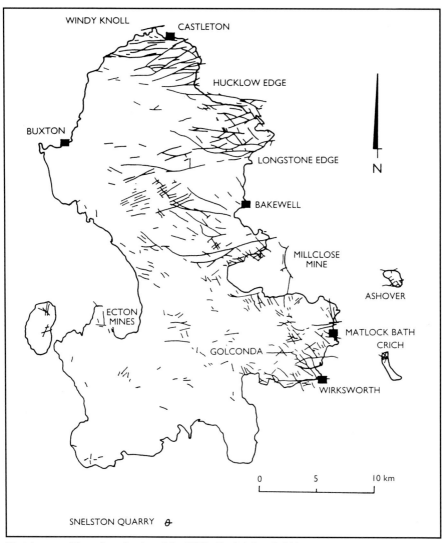

Sketch map of the mineral veins of the White Peak (after Quirk).

disposed of both waste rock and water therein. A few mine-cum-caverns are open to the public today. Examples are the Speedwell Cavern at Castleton, and the Masson and Rutland Caverns at Matlock. Bagshaw Cavern is entered via an old lead mine. Temple Mine at Matlock has some small natural caves partly full of sand.

Good examples of country crossed by mineral veins are the Old Moor and Linicar west of Castleton and Pindale east of the same village. The Magpie Mine site near

38 |

Layered fluorspar and baryte. Masson Mines, Matlock. The light coloured baryte surrounds the darker fluorspar

A cavity lined with large calcite crystals. Masson Mines, Matlock

The ruined pumping engine house and chimney, Magpie Mine, Sheldon. The engine house dates from 1868

Iron-stained white baryte with fluorspar. A stringer in the Clayton ore deposit at Ecton Mine, in limestone host rock, photographed in the adit just above river level. The fluorspar contains minute crystals of chalcopyrite (copper and iron sulphide, $CuFeS_2$)

Sheldon has a complex of poorly exposed veins with numerous relics of 19th century mine buildings. Adjacent to the National Stone Centre at Wirksworth, the Gulf has a series of parallel veins marked by many waste heaps.

Whilst lead mining is uneconomic today, fluorspar and barytes are produced in large amounts, from both opencasts and underground mines mainly around Castleton,

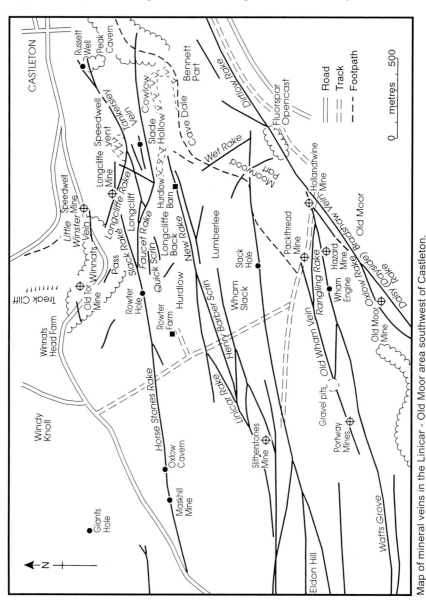

Map of mineral veins in the Linicar - Old Moor area southwest of Castleton.

Eyam and Stony Middleton. As a general rule, fluorspar is most common in the eastern ends of the veins, baryte in the middle and calcite to the west, so that mining for the products is similarly concentrated.

Amongst the minerals is the variety of fluorspar called **Blue John**. With its banded blue/purple and yellow/white colouring it has been mined in the caverns of Treak

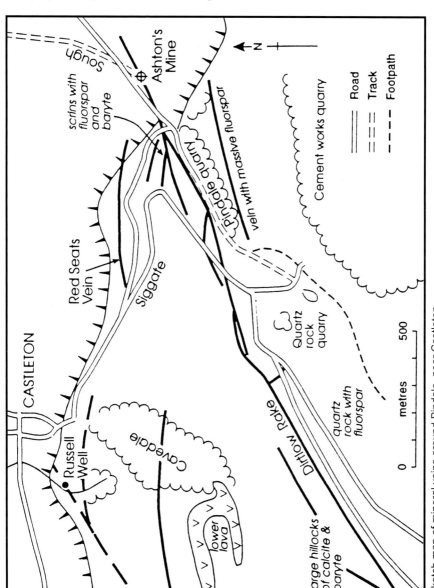

Sketch map of mineral veins around Pindale, near Castleton.

Cliff near Castleton since the 18th century. Used for the manufacture of ornaments and jewellery, small quantities are still produced today.

A long-standing controversy occurs around how the minerals were deposited. Galena, fluorspar, baryte, calcite, sphalerite and chalcopyrite are almost insoluble in pure water but they all show the physical characteristics of having crystallized from fluid solutions. However, studies of the microscopic inclusions of trapped fluid show that the mineralizing fluids were highly saline (up to ten times more salty than the sea), they were slightly oily, and they were at temperatures generally between 70°C and 140°C at the time of crystallization. All these factors greatly increase solubility and the minerals were carried to their sites of deposition in hot, oily brines. When these met fresher and cooler ground-waters, possibly with some sulphate in the rocks, the fluids reacted and the minerals were precipitated in any available void.

The mineralizing fluids are generally thought to have been derived from nearby basins full of muddy sediment where they picked up minute quantities of the necessary elements from mineral grains as they were altered by the heat and pressures of being deeply buried. The fluids were squeezed out from the muddy sediments into the limestone mass by the weight of overlying rocks and by the stresses of Earth movements. There the fluids met cooler, oxygen-bearing waters and probably some sulphurous compounds. Complex chemical reactions took place and minerals were deposited as crystals growing inwards from the walls of voids such as the fissures caused by faulting or in ancient caves. The process was slow but seems to have taken place towards the end of Carboniferous times, about 290 million years ago, when the limestone was buried under at least 2 km of younger strata, the Millstone Grit and Coal Measures. It was about this period that the Pennine sedimentary basin was undergoing the beginnings of "inversion" to an uplift which eventually became the Pennine Hills. Subsequent erosion of the Millstone Grit and Coal Measures has exposed the limestone and the mineral veins at the surface.

Apart from the base metals, there have been mines for several other mineral products. Ochre, umber and wad (impure oxides of iron and manganese) were exploited as constituents of paint, mainly in the Elton - Brassington areas. A small amount of rather earthy iron ore was mined near Hartington station, on what is now the Tissington Trail. Fine-grained dark limestones were mined around Ashford-in-the-Water for use as black marble. Banded rosewood marble and spotted bird's eye marble were obtained nearby. "Figured" or crinoidal marble was quarried around Monyash and small amounts are still raised near Wirksworth. A banded brown variety of baryte was mined near the Arborlow Stone circle as "oakstone" used for ornamental purposes. Chert was mined under much of the Bakewell area for use as a grinding medium in the Potteries. High-purity limestone has been mined near Middleton-by-Wirksworth since 1959.

In addition to materials mined underground, Derbyshire is one of Britain's most quarried counties, and there are large quarries for limestone used as aggregate or in the chemical industry, shale for use in cement works, and sandstone for building and abrasives. Together they make a landscape all of their own.

The relics of the mine-workings and associated buildings, waste heaps, drainage soughs and quarries are a distinctive part of our landscape today.

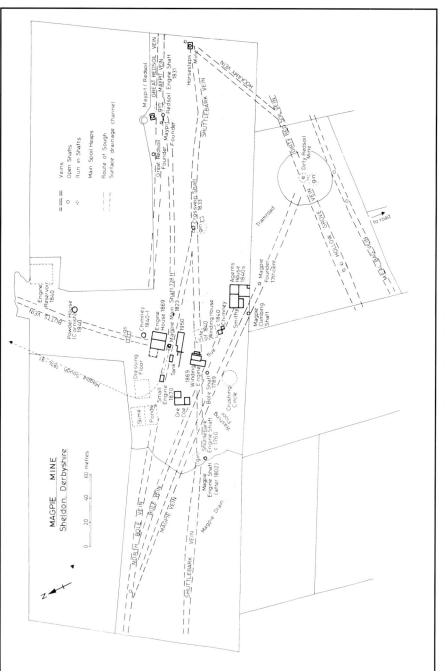

Sketch map of mineral veins, mines and buildings at the Magpie Mine, Sheldon.

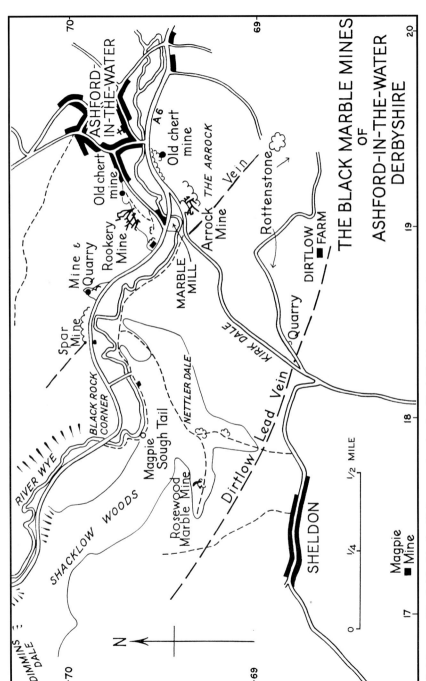

Sketch map of the Ashford-in-the-Water area showing the Black Marble and other mines.

6

Before the Ice Age:
The Pocket Deposits

Little is known of what happened in the Peak District during the first 58 million years of the last great epoch of geological time, the Cenozoic, as it was essentially a period of uplift with erosion removing the cover of younger strata from the infant Pennines. The retreating escarpments of the cover strata included an escarpment of the Sherwood Sandstones of Triassic age, which shed erosion products on to the limestone plateau. These are represented by the silica sands and clays of the so-called Pocket Deposits around Brassington, Friden and the Weaver Hills.

The sands and clays of the **Pocket Deposits, or Brassington Formation** as they should strictly be called, are now found in collapsed solution hollows high on the limestone plateau. Some sixty of these have been quarried for the silica sands, which were used in the manufacture of refractory bricks for furnace linings. Though scattered over an area some 30 km wide, the infillings of the solution hollows are so similar across this width that they must have once formed a continuous sheet over at least the southern half of the Peak District. The sands contain scattered quartzite pebbles which are clearly derived from the erosion of the retreating escarpment of Triassic sandstones, now seen in various outcrops around Hulland Ward and along the Trent Valley. Sheets of sand with pebbles were spread out by streams flowing from the Triassic escarpment on to the limestone before being carried away by one or more rivers draining towards the North Sea. The sands were covered by a succession of coloured and grey clays as the highest strata of the Brassington Formation and these can be found in the few of the pockets. The grey clays contain fossil plant material ranging from large branches of Sequoia trees, to scraps of heathers, mosses and pollen, representing a heathland vegetation in contrast to what one would expect on limestone. The fossil plants permit an approximate geological date to be placed on the Brassington Formation - around the boundary of Miocene and Pliocene times, some 7 million years ago. At some date after this, weathering by solution of the limestone beneath the sands caused the collapse of the unconsolidated sheets of sediment into hollows as much as a hundred metres wide and deep. Whether any of these were in fact collapsed caves once is debatable. The remaining uncollapsed sheets surrounding the pockets were later eroded away so that only the collapsed remnants survive today.

A few of the Pockets show the sands and clays of the Brassington Formation resting on either a coarse chert gravel or on patches of black or lilac-coloured shale, both usually seen trapped between the sand fill and the walls of the pits. The chert gravel is the

Coloured clays of the Brassington Formation. Bees Nest Pit

Silica-sand workings in one of the Brassington Pockets

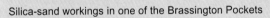

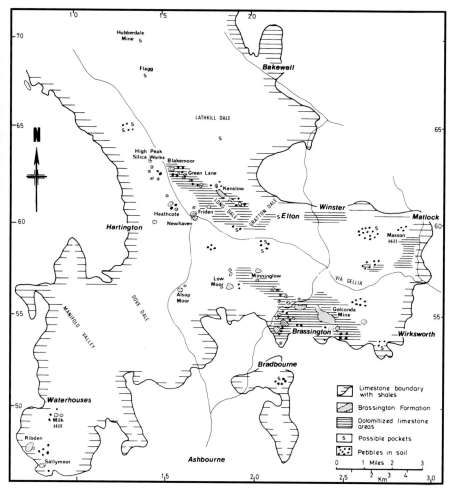

Sketch map of the Brassington Formation and Pockets in the southern part of the White Peak.

insoluble residue of the weathering of the uppermost limestone beds. When these limestones are dissolved the chert nodules are left behind. The shale patches are the last relics of the former cover of Millstone Grit strata, black in its fresh state but with its topmost layers coloured lilac by warm climate weathering long before the Ice Age.

The plateau with the Pockets today is at about 300-350 m altitude but at the time they were forming the limestone surface must have been much lower for the eroded Triassic material to be washed on to it. The corollary to this is that the limestone plateau has been uplifted by at least 200 m since 7 million years ago.

The silica sand pockets provide us with an unusual landscape for a limestone plateau, particularly with heathland vegetation in patches surrounded by limestone grassland.

A climb up Harborough Rocks near Brassington will permit a view over a landscape largely resulting from these pockets and the industrial exploitation thereof. Close by is the firebrick factory which used the sands. Other pockets, almost emptied of their sand fill, are at Blakelow, some 3 km north of Friden. Several pockets lie around Friden itself but most have been filled in with rubbish. A pit at Low Moor south of Pikehall was partly filled in with chemical wastes, but this was unwise as the chemicals were liable to filter through the remaining sands and the underlying limestone to re-appear in spring waters elsewhere. An isolated group of pockets is around Ribden on the Weaver Hills and most of these have also been filled with rubbish.

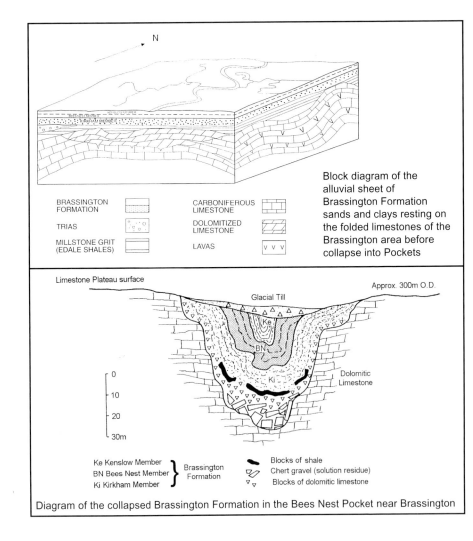

N

Block diagram of the alluvial sheet of Brassington Formation sands and clays resting on the folded limestones of the Brassington area before collapse into Pockets

BRASSINGTON FORMATION

TRIAS

MILLSTONE GRIT (EDALE SHALES)

CARBONIFEROUS LIMESTONE

DOLOMITIZED LIMESTONE

LAVAS

V V V

Limestone Plateau surface

Approx. 300m O.D.

Glacial Till

Ke

BN

Ki

Dolomitic Limestone

0

10

20

30m

Ke Kenslow Member
BN Bees Nest Member } Brassington Formation
Ki Kirkham Member

Blocks of shale
Chert gravel (solution residue)
Blocks of dolomitic limestone

Diagram of the collapsed Brassington Formation in the Bees Nest Pocket near Brassington

7

The Great Ice Age

Our landscape is formed of rocks from the ancient past, but its present-day shape is the result of processes of erosion by water, wind and frost in the last million years or so. By far the most important effect is what happened during the Ice Age.

The last 1.8 million years, known to geologists as the **Pleistocene Period of the Quaternary Era**, was the latest phase of a series when the Earth, in its long history, went through periods of much reduced temperature known as ice ages. In fact the ice accumulated at the Poles and in mountainous regions to a far greater extent than the present Arctic and Antarctic ice sheets. The Arctic ice cap expanded to cover much of Northern Europe and North America. Glaciers spread outwards from Scandinavia, the Alps and the Rocky Mountains to cover much of lowland Europe and the North American prairies, merging until they became slowly moving sheets of ice hundreds of metres thick sliding over all before them eventually to melt away in mid-latitudes. The moving ice sheets tore up rocks and ground them up providing vast amounts of rock debris. This was eventually either washed out at the margins and dumped as moraines or was simply left when the ice melted to blanket the countryside with a mixture of mud and rocks known as boulder clay (known as till to geologists). Melt-water streams discharged sheets of gravel, sand and mud around the contemporary margins of the ice sheets. Some of these survive as terminal moraines and outwash plains, though not in the Peak District. River systems dating from before the ice advances were largely obliterated and their valleys filled in; soil and vegetation was removed and animal life decimated or driven south to warmer climates.

When an ice sheet melts away it is said to have retreated, but this does not mean that it went into reverse movement: instead it melted faster than it moved forwards so the margin retreated. More or less complete melts led to interglacial episodes which lasted for thousands of years.

In Britain ice sheets extended as far south as the northern outskirts of London, and some reached the Bristol Channel area in the west; floating ice even reached the Scilly Isles. During the Pleistocene period there was not just one advance of the ice sheet but several. Ocean floor deposits suggest perhaps as many as twenty advances and retreats but on land the record is incomplete. Opinions vary but at least four major glacial advances can be identified in parts of both Europe and North America, with warm interglacial phases of temperate climate restored between them. As each ice advance tends to sweep away the products of the earlier ones, much of the evidence is destroyed

Elderbush Cave, Manifold Valley. Excavations revealed a long period of occupation by prehistoric man and animals

A sand-filled cave in Masson Hill, Matlock

High Tor, Matlock

Boulder Clay. Shining Bank Quarry. Lathkill Dale

The solifluction deposits on the floor of the Rushup Valley (see page 53)

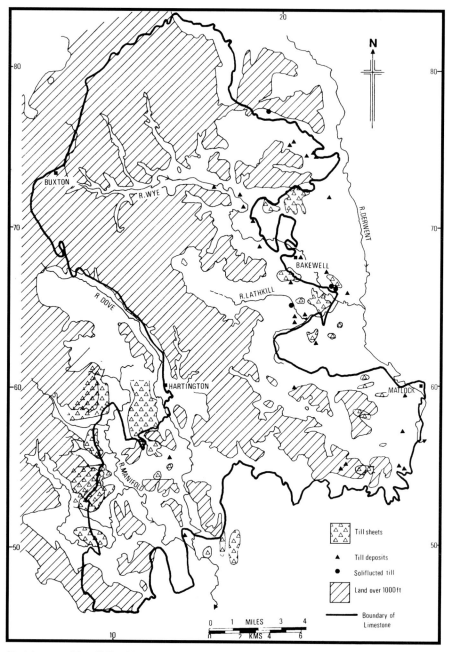

Sketch map of the till (boulder clay) areas in the Peak District (after Burek).

and interpreting the remnants raises many problems. Only two major advances are now recognized in Britain, the Anglian and the Devensian, though there is some evidence for other lesser advances both before and between these. A pre-Anglian cold phase is known only from a few deposits in East Anglia; some cave deposits in the Peak District hint at the same pre-Anglian glaciation. The **Anglian glacial phase**, represented mainly by deposits in East Anglia, lasted from about 470 000 to 420 000 years ago and its ice sheet certainly covered the Peak District. Details of a Wolstonian advance around 150 000 to 120 000 years ago are difficult to interpret and controversial. The **Devensian advance** was the last ice advance lasting from about 80 000 to 10 000 years ago; it is represented by deposits in Cheshire (Deva was the Roman name for Chester) and its ice reached only as far south as York on the east and south Staffordshire on the west, so that the Peak District escaped the effects of scouring by glaciers in the Devensian phase. However, it suffered an Arctic tundra climate during this last cold period, with plenty of snowfields on frozen ground which bore sparse vegetation.

In each ice advance, ice caps accumulated on the Scottish Highlands, Lake District, North Pennines and North Wales, and the main ice streams moved southwards on either side of the Pennines. In the Anglian glaciation overflows of ice crossed the Peak District, but the movement was sluggish and did not erode the typical features of a glacierized landscape, so we have no corries or U-shaped valleys. Instead the Peak District became an area with somewhat limited boulder clay cover. The higher Dark Peak acted as a shield protecting the White Peak and ice movement was even more sluggish there, with very little boulder clay left behind. The Peak District's boulder clay is thought to be almost all from the Anglian advance, with only marginal effects from earlier episodes. Boulder clay from the Devensian glaciation shows that ice reached the western margins of the Dark Peak west of Glossop and Chapel-en-le-Frith but no further.

Good examples of boulder clay in the White Peak may be seen as the overburden is stripped off the tops of some limestone quarries as the faces advance. Up to 8 metres of boulder clay forms the terrace above the Wye Valley from Bakewell to Rowsley; it can be seen capping the face at Shining Bank Quarry near Alport-by-Youlgrave.

The cold climate of the Devensian phase did not bring glaciers across the Peak District, but repeated freezing and thawing of the ground surface resulted in the sludge known as solifluction deposits (or "head" on some geological maps). A sheet of this floors the Rushup Valley, partly masking the limestone/shale contact. Later streams have cut channels into this leading to swallets at the limestone boundary.

Traces of a pre-Anglian glaciation in the Peak District around 700 000 to 1 million years ago are known only from cave deposits near Castleton, at Matlock and in the Manifold Valley. The first two are sands washed into the caves at the margin of the ice wherein a geological feature has been recognized which probably dates from around 780 000 years ago. Elderbush Cave in the Manifold Valley has a hiatus in the stalagmite record at about the same time. The break in stalagmite growth is thought to represent a cold phase when the ground was frozen and no percolation took place. These three observations demonstrate the presence of a cold climate but give few clues about the size, thickness or duration of any ice sheet then. At best it seems likely that the sands in caves at Castleton and Matlock were the products of outwash from melting ice.

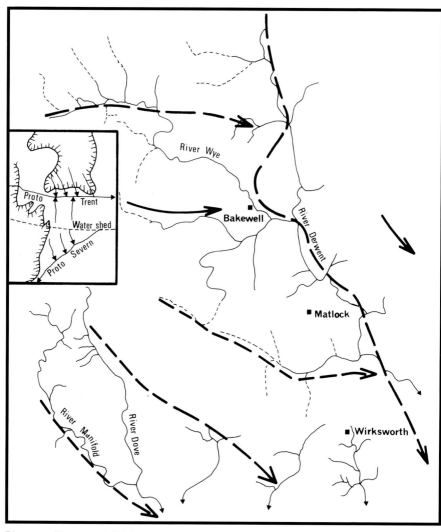

Diagram of the pre-glacial river pattern across the South Pennines.
The regional relationships are shown in the inset (after Burek).

Monsal Dale eroded by the River Wye - the only major river to cross the White Peak (see page 56)

Cavedale, Castleton: a dry gorge cut through reef - limestones (see page 56)

8

Rivers and Drainage

Little is known of the pre-glacial river pattern, but it is likely that the 6 million years since the formation of the Pocket Deposits was a period of erosion with a pattern of shallow river valleys being eroded into the highest parts of the Peak District and draining eastwards towards the North Sea. The Anglian glaciers crossed this riverine landscape from north to south, with glacial deposits filling in the shallow valleys and diverting drainage. As the ice sheet melted, it seems to have done so in the east first, so that the post-Anglian rivers flowed that way, and partly restored the pattern of pre-glacial east-flowing drainage. Relics may be seen as the present day pattern of the east-flowing River Noe in Edale and Hope Valley, the River Wye from Buxton to Bakewell, the River Lathkill, and the Via Gellia Valley. This system of parallel river courses drained the Peak District at high level and once continued through wind-gaps in the Millstone Grit escarpments. However, the headward growth of the River Derwent had the advantage of being on unresistant shales for most of its course and it progressively "captured" the middle sectors of the older rivers. Progressive incision of the Derwent cut a new valley which drained from north to south along the thick belt of shales between the White Peak and the Millstone Grit ridges of the East Moors. Over to the west the Rivers Dove and Manifold evolved north to south courses comparable to the Derwent and it appears that all three of these major Peak District rivers are largely young, post-Anglian features developed as tributaries to the River Trent.

Between the cold icy phases there were the interglacial phases. Each was a period of tens of thousands of years with a climate much like today's, possibly even warmer at times, as hippo remains have been found in the London area. Weathering processes were much like today's and rivers were gradually incised further into the plateau, developing the pattern of present day drainage from a combination of east-flowing melt-water streams and south-flowing tributaries of the Trent. The rivers slowly eroded their valleys deeper but in so doing they often meandered from side to side widening the valleys. Thus they left terraces and bevelled spurs on valley sides. The higher parts of Bakewell are built on such a terrace.

Another aspect of river erosion is that the process commenced on the sandstones and shales of the Millstone Grit and as they eroded their way through this they met an irregular surface of limestone and cut gorges through some upstanding limestone masses. The Derwent Gorge at Matlock is a fine example. Another is the middle section of Bradwell Dale. Where the limestone surface was diversified by the presence of reefs the phenomenon of entrapment of river courses occurred and "anomalous gorges" resulted. The River Dove wends a meandering course between limestone

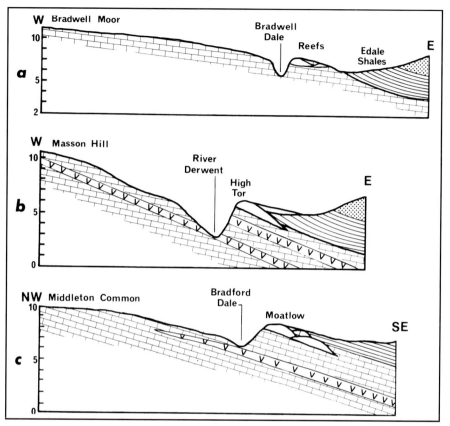

Sections across some anomalous gorges where rivers have been incised from the former shale cover into the limestone and were trapped up slope by reefs.

mud-mounds in a north-south belt of reefs. At first the river flowed along a shale belt but as it eroded deeper it was shifted sideways as each reef-mound was exhumed, and it now follows a winding course between mound-like crags.

The main rivers received a boost from the excess melt-water from the snowfields and tundra in the Devensian cold phase. Those rivers rising in the Millstone Grit country and flowing on to the limestone were loaded with abrasive sand and were incised faster. The Rivers Wye, Dove and Manifold produced deep gorges for much of their length. Much of the Derwent's course has terraces and meanders on the shales, though at Matlock it too developed a gorge through the limestone, being trapped by the High Tor reef.

A case can been made out for part of the middle course of the Derwent having changed owing to glacier diversion. Its original course was from near Calver almost into Bakewell to join the Wye, but a late advance of an Anglian glacier down the Wye Valley from Buxton blocked this route and the river found a more direct route via Chatsworth Park.

9

Dry Valleys

During the Devensian cold tundra phase, the melt-water from melting snowfields ran across frozen ground and streams cut into the limestone surface. Each eroded its own valley but when the cold phase ended and there were no longer any melting snowfields, these valleys lost their catchments and streams. What little drainage remained went underground into caves, leaving a network of **dry valleys** over much of the White Peak. Some carry ephemeral streams in very wet weather. Both the Rivers Lathkill and Manifold disappear underground for parts of their courses except in very wet weather. The Monks Dale and Cressbrook Dale tributaries to the Wye are classic dry valleys, with only limited surface drainage where underlying volcanic rocks prevent the streams sinking underground.

The Winnats Pass at Castleton is an unusual deep gorge-like dry valley with a very small catchment to account for the depth of erosion. But, if at some stage ice was dammed up in the Rushup Valley, melt water could have been much more effective.

The gorge sector of Bradwell Dale is dry as drainage goes underground via a sink hole (swallet) further up the valley and the water resurges some 2 km downtream in the village.

Other dry valleys include Taddington Dale and Deepdale, both tributaries to the Wye Valley; Gratton Dale and Hay Dale, tributaries to the River Bradford; and the reaches of the Via Gellia.

Lathkill Head Cave showing the River Lathkilldale, which only emerges here in times of high rainfall

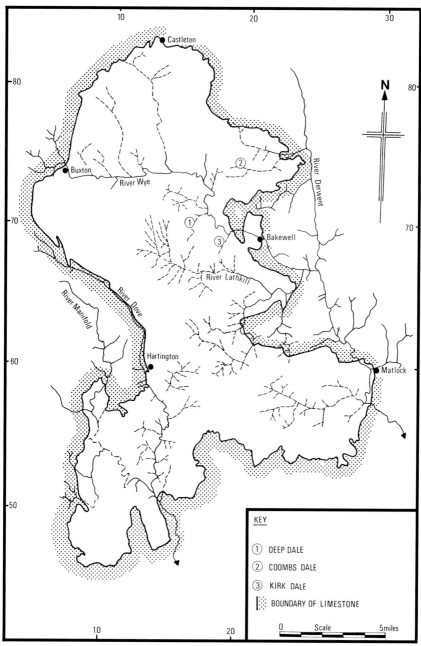

Sketch map of the dry valleys of the White Peak (after Warwick) with a few classic
examples indicated.

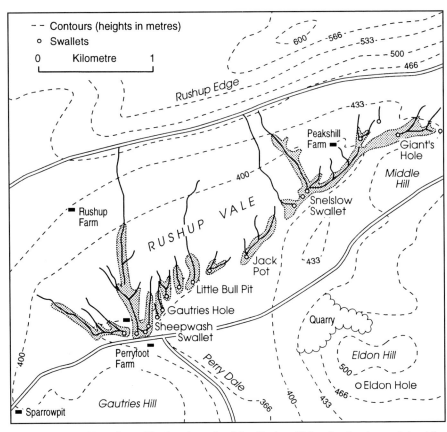

Channels incised into the solifluction deposits of the Rushup Valley, leading to swallets at the limestone margin.

10

Edges and Tors

As rivers wear their courses down into the alternating sandstones and shales of the Millstone Grit, they leave escarpments along the higher flanks of the valleys. These are the gritstone edges so beloved of climbers, with well-known examples in the Roaches, around Kinder Scout plateau, and the Derwent and Stanage Edges. The cliff faces retreat by percolating water seeping out at the base of the porous sandstone where it rests on shale. Blocks are undermined and tumble off to form block-fields (sometimes known as clitter) down the lower slopes. Many of these blocks were quarried in the past to make grind stones for use in Sheffield's tool and cutlery industries and unfinished examples may be seen below Stanage and Millstone Edges.

Tors are isolated blocks of gritstone on top of some edges. They are erosional residuals left when the surrounding rock has disintegrated. Wind, rain and frost have etched them into weird shapes, and the rotted rock has been washed away to yield fantastic shapes such as the Coach & Horses on Derwent Edge and "Mother Cap" near the Surprise View. Robin Hood's Stride is one of the best tors in the area around Stanton and Birchover.

Dolomite Tors are comparable shapes developed on the dolomitized areas of the White Peak's limestone. Weathering in cold wet climatic conditions removes the calcite from the partly dolomitized limestone and leaves loose dolomite-sand. This either sludges downhill under solifluction (free and thaw conditions) conditions or is washed away by rainwater, both under peri-glacial conditions when there is little soil or vegetation. Removal of the loose sand leaves residual cores standing above the general level of the plateau. Dolomite tors are most common around Winster, Longcliffe and Brassington in the southern half of the White Peak.

Robin Hood s Stride, a typical gritstone tor

A dolomite tor near Winster

Dovedale

11

Loess

Much of the White Peak has a sub-soil cover on the limestone consisting of fine-grained silty clay. Revealed in many temporary excavations, microscopic studies show that the material is wind-blown dust derived from the surrounding Millstone Grit country during peri-glacial (tundra) conditions. The lack of vegetation then would expose the sandstones and shales of the Millstone Grit to the blast of Arctic gales. Doubtless much of the Millstone Grit country has the same cover but it is so like weathered bedrock that it has not usually been distinguished. This wind-blown dust is widespread in Europe where it is known as loess. The Peak District equivalent has an admixture of insoluble residue from the underlying limestone. A good place to see it is in various mineral diggings on the Old Moor west of Castleton. A blanket up to a metre thick is common lying on the limestone and is covered by the turf. Much of the loess washed down into caves as the frozen ground thawed out and this accounts for the muddy conditions in Derbyshire's caves, so well-known to cave explorers.

Loessic clay beneath an old soil layer (mine waste above). Old Moor, near Castleton

12

The Peak District in the late Ice Age

We can picture the scenario around 10 000 years ago as a cold, bleak landscape with a sparse vegetation of Arctic Willow, hazel, sedges and mosses and much bare ground. A few mammals were around including mammoth, woolly rhinoceros, deer, wolves, bears, and foxes; their bones are found in cave entrances. The smaller mammals used caves as dens, but scavengers such as hyenas also dragged the carcases in. The Old Stone Age (Palaeolithic) human population was probably no more than a few dozen existing under hostile conditions but they still managed to leave a few of their stone implements in caves.

The Ice Age effectively ended some 10 000 years ago, though it was some time before the climate returned to normal. The post-glacial period saw the final touches put to the Peak District landscape. As vegetation returned so did mammals and, in due course, hunters. Much of the White Peak was scrubby grassland with a patchy cover of bushes and small trees. By about 3500 B.C. the concept of agriculture filtered through from the Mediterranean area and farming started, particularly on the grassy White Peak. River valleys were mostly avoided as they were too boggy and much of the Millstone Grit country was too rugged for farming. Caves provided shelter for Neolithic farmers and, later on, for Bronze Age and Iron Age man. Remains of settlements, burial places and religious sites (e.g. Arborlow stone circle) dot the uplands. The farmers transformed the landscape to one where human influence is everywhere present, wild as it may seem today.

13

Landslips

A part of the process of valley erosion is the slipping of unstable masses of rock from their sides. Such mass movements are known as landslips or landslides and there are some spectacular examples in the Dark Peak. The best known is at **Mam Tor**, about 2 km west of Castleton. Here a mass of sandstones and shales of the lower Millstone Grit slipped into the head of Hope Valley in post-glacial (Holocene) times, probably four or five thousand years ago. The scar from which the rock mass fell is over 150 metres high and the debris flowed out for at least a kilometre. A packhorse road was built across the broken ground about 1810 and was unwisely enlarged and "improved" for modern traffic in the 1930s. In post-war years as heavier traffic used the road and as more and more water seeped into the broken ground it became even more unstable and movements broke the road surface necessitating frequent road repairs. Eventually the road was abandoned in 1979 and a walk over the distorted tarmac today is a lesson on where not to build a road. The average movement today is around a metre every four years.

Cold Side and Back Tor are other comparable landslips along the Edale side of the adjoining Losehill to Rushup Edge ridge. Though there are no main roads involved, these two slips are still mobile and the side road over Cold Side requires repair at intervals.

Many other landslips are scattered around the Millstone Grit country. **Alport Castles** in a side valley north of Ladybower Reservoir are a spectacular series of crags where a large slab has become detached from the escarpment behind. A further series of landslips lies along **Longdendale**. Less obvious and older slips occur below many Millstone Grit escarpments, for example on the slopes above Matlock Bath station, near Cromford and at **Black Rocks** above Wirksworth.

The White Peak too has its landslips. Perhaps the best known is **Hobs House** in Monsal Dale, where a mass of thin-bedded limestone has moved forward into the valley. The nearby Cressbrookdale has the slipped mass of **Peters Stone**, near Wardlow. Both of these appear to have moved on thin volcanic clay wayboards. Parts of the western slopes of the Derwent Gorge at Matlock are old slips and a crag slid off opposite High Tor in the 1960s and ruined two houses.

Thin pro-delta sandstones and shales. Mam Tor, Castleton

Alport Castles landslip, near
Ladybower Reservoir

Back Tor landslip, Edale

The broken Tarmac of the Mam Tor road

Lud Church near Gradback, south of the River Dane is a classic example of movement creating a chasam

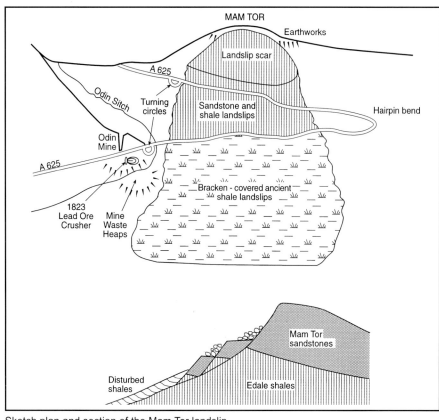

Sketch plan and section of the Mam Tor landslip.

14

Tufa

When rainwater soaks into limestone country it may form cave systems (see later) or it may simply carry away some of the lime from limestone in solution. When such water reappears as springs it is sometimes so loaded with calcium carbonate in solution that the latter is deposited again as tufa. Furthermore, there is some evidence of mildly thermal waters rising from deep within the limestone and dissolving limestone en route. Again the springs may deposit tufa. The reasons for tufa deposition are that the water carries the carbonate in solution as calcium bicarbonate and when it meets the air it loses carbon dioxide to the atmosphere and carbonate is precipitated. This process is often enhanced by lowly plants such as mosses taking up carbon dioxide and providing surfaces for encrustations of tufa. Further enhancement is caused by cooling as warm thermal waters resurge.

The best known tufa deposits are around the slightly warm (21° C) springs at Matlock Bath, where the tufa encrusts objects placed in it. The so-called **Petrifying Well** could have as much as 5 mm thickness of tufa deposited on top-hats, birds nests etc in a few years. The nearby Via Gellia valley has a spring which deposited enough tufa to be quarried and the unusual **Tufa Cottage** is built of large blocks of tufa. Tufa was also quarried in Monsal Dale and blocks were used for rockeries, including the Winter Gardens at Blackpool. Parts of Lathkill Dale are floored by tufa deposits, as much as 11 m thick as shown by a recent borehole. Limited tufa is still being deposited in the stream bed at **Alport-by-Youlgreave**. The crag north of the road at Alport is an old tufa deposit which looks so like a limestone cliff that it is often mis-interpreted: about 50 m long and 5 m high it shows typical tufa features normally only present under water. A tufa sheet floors the stream at Wormhill Springs in Chee Dale where the excess lime may have come form the former lime works at Peak Dale. Similar modern tufa occurs in the dale bottom at Harpur Hill near Buxton, where the lime again comes from former lime-works operations.

Left: Peters Stone landslip, Cressbrookdale

15

Screes

The action of frost on many exposed limestone cliffs is to shatter the rock and the debris falls to the lower slopes to accumulate as scree. Well-known screes mantle the hillsides in the Winnats Pass, Cavedale, Millers Dale, Monsal Dale, Lathkill Dale, Dovedale and the Manifold Valley. In the latter, at Ecton, the screes have been partly cemented together by tufa-like material deposited in the voids between limestone fragments. This partly cemented scree was once quarried for road-making material. It had a commercial name of 'calcrete'.

In cold winters today, moisture from rain or snow gets into cracks in cliff faces and when it freezes it expands and gradually wedges off bits of limestone. So the formation of scree is still going on today.

The quarry on the right of this photograph worked a huge scree deposit laid down on a bend in the River Manifold at Ecton. It is known locally as calcrete

16
Peat

The cover of peat is one of the notable features of Pennine moors, often forming wide areas of boggy ground known as peat-bogs. Examples of peat bogs are on Kinder Scout, Derwent Moors, Ringinglow Bog, Goldsitch Moss above Buxton, and the East Moor above Chatsworth. Most of the peat-bogs have two or three metres of sodden rotted heather, sphagnum moss and grasses lying above bed-rock. A few peat-bogs have as much as ten metres of peat, e.g. Ringinglow Bog. The peat often contains pollen which can be dated to provide a record of changes in plant cover according to climatic variation.

Most Pennine peats started growth after the Ice Age. Maximum growth was during a period of lush vegetation growth in a slightly warmer period than today's climate between 8000 and 6500 years ago, i.e. about 6000-4500 B.C. Cooler conditions then set in and peat accumulation slowed to a minimum before erosion set in some 5000 years ago.

In the last 2000 years or so higher rainfall has caused the sodden peat-bogs to burst at the edges and gulleys have eroded back to yield a pattern of meandering channels known as groughs. Peat-digging, hikers' feet, heather-burning, drainage channels and grazing have accentuated gulley formation until there is a network of gulleys over most peat-bogs. Many gulleys are cut through to gritstone bedrock which breaks up to yield white quartz sand. Atmospheric pollution since the Industrial Revolution has killed some of the vegetation and large areas of peat are now bare. With today's acid rain, erosion is accelerating, though global warming may one day reverse this trend.

Peat deposit
on Kinder
Scout

17

Caves

Caves are underground extensions of surface scenery; indeed if caves collapse the resultant holes can be very much part of the scenery, though fortunately this is rare in the Peak District. Although some 250 caves (and hundreds of old lead mines) are recorded in the White Peak, our limestones are not exactly riddled with holes like gorgonzola cheese as many think. Most of the caves are short and only a score or so are extensive enough to appeal to cave explorers and speleologists.

Eight caves are open to the public with guided tours: four at Castleton (Peak, Speedwell, Treak Cliff and Blue John Caverns); one at Bradwell (Bagshaw Cavern); one at Buxton (Poole's Cavern); and two at Matlock (Rutland and Masson Caverns). Except for these you should not attempt to explore caves without proper equipment (lamps and protective clothing) and under the guidance of an experienced caver. Bagshaw Cavern provides an adventure caving trip as well a tourist visit.

Caves provide us with much of interest in landscape evolution. They are part of the natural drainage of limestone country and some are still active with underground streams in them. Others have been abandoned by their streams and may have been partly filled in by sediments or are gradually being filled by stalactite and stalagmite formations (known as speleothems to speleologists).

If caves open on to hillsides they have sometimes been occupied by animals or by prehistoric man, and the entrance deposits are then the subject of detailed study by archaeologists. Both Old and New Stone Age relics have been found in cave entrances, as well as evidence of inhabitation by Bronze, Iron Age and Romano-British people. Indeed at least one cave was still inhabited in the 18th century. Rope-makers worked in Peak Cavern until the end of the 20th century.

Caves, particularly entrances, may be occupied by present day animals, predominantly insects. Various worms and crustaceans spend much if not all of their lives in caves. Microbes dwell in some and provide food for the larger animals. Bio-speleologists have listed some hundreds of species from Peak District caves, though many of their life cycles are not fully understood as yet. Badgers and foxes occupy a few caves. plus bats, flying out on summer evenings to catch insects.

Speleogenesis is the process of the origin and development of caves. As soon as a limestone mass is exposed by uplift above sea level, rainwater can percolate through pores and joints to resurge lower down as springs. Rainwater is very weak carbonic acid and slowly dissolves limestone. Sometimes the acidity can be enhanced by

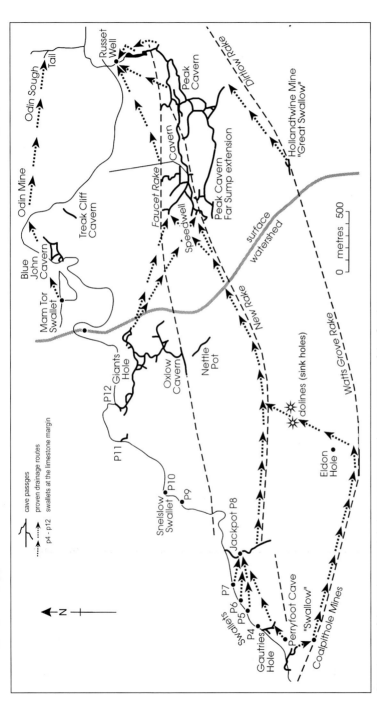

Sketch map of the underground drainage pattern and cave systems of the Castleton area.

Nan Tor, Manifold Valley, riddled with short caves

The main stream cave in Peak Cavern, Castleton

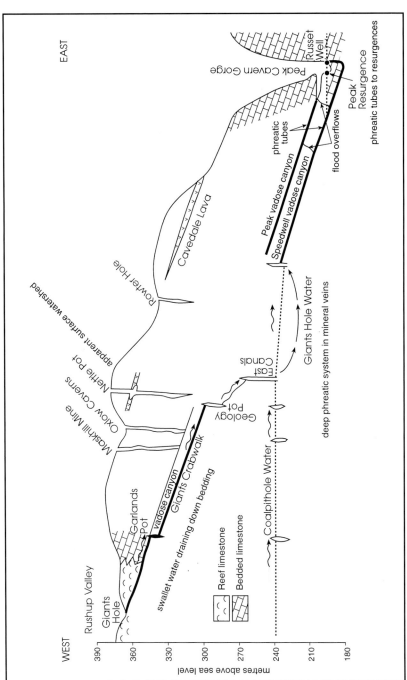

Diagrammatic section of the Giants Hole to Speedwell and Peak Cavern cave system.

sulphuric acid resulting from the oxidation of pyrite dispersed in black shales. At first cave inception is in miniature: pores are enlarged and joints widened very slowly so that water movement is very slow. But if bedding planes contain a little shale (with pyrite) between limestone beds, early cave development is accelerated. As soon as one or more pathways through the limestone mass are sufficiently enlarged to allow running water to pass through, then much more rapid erosion takes place and cave passages evolve. Whilst still filled with water the conditions are said to be **phreatic** and solutional enlargement takes place in all directions. But as surface valleys are incised, some of the water drains out of the limestone mass and passages are filled with air above a flowing stream: these are **vadose** conditions and abrasive sediment may be washed in to erode still further. Vadose erosion takes place downwards in the floor of the stream and as valley incision permits lower surface outlets to become operative, early passages are abandoned, and new streamways take over. A few caves develop entirely from percolation over a wide area, but more often surface streams drain off adjacent rocks and boost erosion by being more acidic and by washing in abrasive sand and gravel.

The above course of events has resulted in two major stream caves near Castleton, the **Peak and Speedwell** cave systems, now totalling some 15 km of passages. Water enters through a series of swallet caves along the limestone/shale boundary in Rushup Valley, notably via Giants Hole. The cave streams reappear in daylight at the Peak Cavern resurgence and at Russet Well nearby; they merge to form Peakshole Water flowing eastwards down Hope Valley. However, there is no route through from swallet to resurgence available to cavers, as the middle courses of the streams go deep into mineral vein cavities in the phreatic zone before rising again. Abandoned upper levels lie above the streamways and some have magnificent stalactite formations. Some ancient mineral vein cavities have also been abandoned by the drainage and are now seen as high vertical caverns, such as the Bottomless Pit Cavern in Speedwell. Only the outer abandoned part of Peak Cavern is shown to tourists and even this is liable to flooding after heavy rain or snow melt. Speedwell Cavern is in fact mostly a half-flooded mine level traversed by boat with a single large natural cavern, the Bottomless Pit. The Speedwell stream caves lie beyond the tourist route. A huge extension of this system has been found recently with a height of some 180m or so.

The **Blue John and Treak Cliff** cave systems represent older stream caves now left high and almost dry as the drainage went deeper. They were partly developed along ancient caves containing mineral deposits, particularly Blue John fluorspar and both caves are a combination of natural cavern and mine workings for Blue John. They are both open to the public.

Open potholes are rare in the Peak District compared with the Yorkshire Dales. In fact the only notable open pothole is Eldon Hole, west of Castleton. The shaft is some 60 metres deep, and a short passage leads into a large inner chamber. Many fallen boulders block the way into deeper caverns recorded in an 18th century account.

Many of the Castleton cave passages are liberally supplied with mud derived from inwashed loess and sand eroded from the Millstone Grit of Rushup Edge.

Once caves are present and no longer subject to frequent flooding, rainwater can

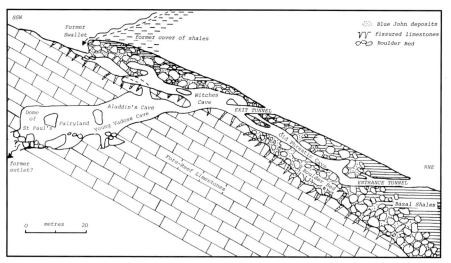

Profile of Treak Cliff Cavern.

still percolate through the roof bringing with it calcium carbonate in solution. If this is deposited within the cave it forms the various types of stalactite and stalagmite which provide impressive subterranean scenery. Stalactites start as straws where the lime is deposited round the droplet as it hangs in the roof. One ring on another makes a tubular straw. Crystal growth within the tube can block it and deflect the flow down the outside, and so the stalactite grows wider. Stalagmites grow on the cave floors when drops fall from the roof and lose their excess carbon dioxide on impact. Pure stalactites are white but most in the Peak District are creamy yellow owing to minute admixtures of iron or of soil derivatives. There are fine examples in the grottoes of Treak Cliff Cavern. Occasional green stalactites are due to traces of copper and blue-grey may reflect a trace of manganese. Stalactites often contain traces of uranium derived from overlying rocks, far too little to give damaging radiation but enough for sophisticated chemical techniques to measure, and the isotopic ratios can give an estimate of the age of the stalactite, and hence a minimum age for when the cave passed from phreatic to vadose conditions. Samples from Treak Cliff Cavern yielded a date of 111 000 years and this means that the cave itself must be much older.

The various underground streams resurging from the Peak District's caves carry an average of about 200 parts per million of calcium carbonate in solution so that they are gradually removing the limestone mass. However, this is only a fraction of the limestone extracted by quarrying for industrial purposes.

Bagshaw Cavern at Bradwell is an underground stream course parallel to and partly beneath Bradwell Dale. Both active and abandoned stream passages are present and some high level grottoes have been discovered. Adventure trips are available here.

Carlswark Cavern is part of a complex series of mostly dry (but very muddy) caves in the limestones around Eyam and Stoney Middleton. Streams sink at various points below Eyam Edge, principally at the partly collapsed Waterfall Swallet. The water resurges from a lead miners' sough near Stoney Middleton church. A long-abandoned relic of an ancient cave is the series of arches near Eyam known as Cucklet Church, where outdoor services were held during the plague of 1665-6.

In **Lathkill Dale**, the river is mainly underground in the upper reaches near Monyash but occasional flooding brings it to the surface from the mouth of Lathkill Head Cave. Several semi-abandoned caves act as flood overflows or tributaries. The lime-rich water deposits tufa at Pudding Springs further down the Dale. Downstream the river disappears again but this is due to mine drainage soughs beneath the valley floor. The underground stream finally resurges from beneath a tufa sheet at Bubble Springs below Over Haddon.

Poole's Cavern at Buxton is open to the public. It is a short semi-abandoned stream cave very well decorated with stalactites and stalagmites. Some of these have an unusual porous texture and "poached egg" colouring apparently due to former lime-burning on the hill above. Poole's Cavern entrance was used by prehistoric animals and the first chamber inside appears to have been a religious site used by Romano-British people.

Matlock has several cave-cum-mine systems. **Rutland and Masson Caverns** are high up on the slopes of Masson Hill. Both extend into old lead and fluorspar mine workings with a long history of mining. The cave passages were active as melt-water stream outlets in the Ice Age and some caves are still full of outwash sands and silts from glaciers. Examples can be seen in Masson Cavern and in Temple Mine.

Fern and Roman Caves on High Tor at Matlock are un-roofed lead-mine workings. Temple Mine in Matlock Bath has some sand-filled caverns. Royal Mine nearby is part of a maze of old lead and fluorspar mines.

Rutland and Masson Caverns and **Temple and Royal Mines** are open to the public.

Dovedale has only a few small caves and the River Dove still flows on the surface, but concealed stream-bed springs boost its flow, so that a future cave system is in the early stages of development beneath the valley sides and floor.

The River **Manifold** disappears underground for several kilometres in its middle course, and cavers have found their way into part of the cave system beneath the valley floor. However, these caves are very liable to flooding and are best avoided. The flooded resurgence system at Ilam (the boil holes) has been penetrated by divers to a distance of about 1/4 mile. Several high level caves are of great archaeological interest, e.g. Thors, Elderbush and Beeston Tor Caves.

Many other caves are scattered around the White Peak some with entrances of archaeological interest. A few quite large caves would have remained unknown but they were broken into by lead miners.

18

Areas of special interest

The **Winnats Pass** at Castleton takes its name from Windgates and it certainly lives up to its name in winter months. It is a short but deep gorge cut through a belt of reef limestones on the northern edge of the White Peak's lagoon. Although somewhat obscured by scree and turf, the Winnats' slopes provide us with a section through the reefs. One mass of reef limestone forms Shining Cliff high on the south side of the Pass; its continuation is in the crags along the crest of Treak Cliff on the north side. Earlier reefs are less easy to see in the lower slopes on both sides of the Pass near the bend. Flat-lying lagoonal limestones can be seen in the highest parts of the Pass, whilst steeply inclined fore-reef limestones are on either side of the Pass near the Speedwell Mine. Fossils are present in some of the screes but colllecting should be left to the experts or soon we will have none left.

The origin of the **Winnats Pass** is a complex story. It started in Carboniferous times as a shallow channel between the reefs swept clear by tides washing in and out. Later the channel was filled with shales of the Millstone Grit as the deltas spread into the sea. Much later, in the Ice Age, a meltwater stream found the weakness provided by the shales and re-excavated the channel. Continued run-off of meltwater whilst the ground was frozen greatly deepened the channel. But after the Ice Age the Pass lost its stream and the little wet weather drainage sinks near the bend and finds its way down into the Speedwell Cave system.

The adjacent hillsides of **Treak Cliff** to the north and **Long Cliff** to the south are the steep outer faces of the reef limestone complex. Treak Cliff is also diversified by its Blue John fluorspar deposits and its caves with their magnificent stalactites. Long Cliff is crossed by mineral veins with lines of old workings. The veins were intersected in the Speedwell Mine.

Mam Tor, west of Castleton, rises to nearly 600 metres above sea level. Crowned by the earthworks of an Iron Age fort, probably used as a place of retreat during strife some 500 years B.C. Look out for the fortified ditch which surrounds the fort. Mam Tor is composed of alternating thin sandstones and shales of the Millstone Grit. Porous sandstones overlying impervious shales is a classic unstable situation and landslipping started long before the Iron Age. Slipping has continued ever since as the earthworks are truncated. A pack horse road was built across the unstable ground in the early 19th century. In the 20th century this road was "improved" and heavy modern traffic aggravated the instablity so that slipping accelerated. Largely rebuilt in 1945, the road cracked and subsided badly in 1977 following two dry summers and a wet winter. Temporary repairs failed to halt movement and the road was closed in 1979. Movement has totalled another 4 metres in the subsequent 20 years. This may seem small but compare it with the movement which has produced the mass of bracken-covered hummocky ground below. Over the last 2 millenia total movement has been around 150 metres.

At the foot of Mam Tor is **Odin Mine**, one of Britain's oldest lead mines. It was probably worked in Roman times, again in the Dark Ages and in Norman times. There are records of mining in the 13th and from the 17th to 19th centuries. Unfortunately little is accessible underground, and then only to specialist mine explorers, but there are surface relics in the form of vast waste heaps and an iron-tyred crushing wheel installed in 1823 at a cost of £38. The narrow gorge is not a natural feature but has resulted from the unroofing of old workings and parts of the mineral vein can still be seen as well as pick marks in the walls.

To the east and west of Mam Tor is the long ridge of Losehill to Rushup Edge. A popular high walk, it

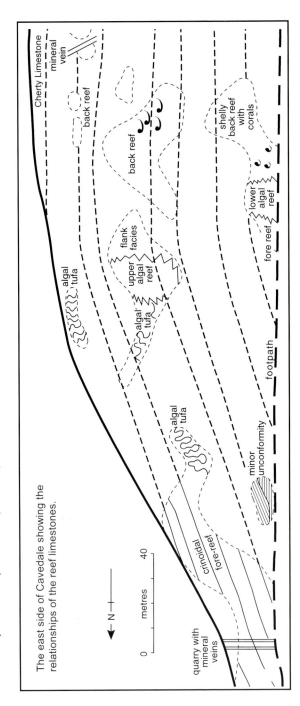

The east side of Cavedale showing the relationships of the reef limestones.

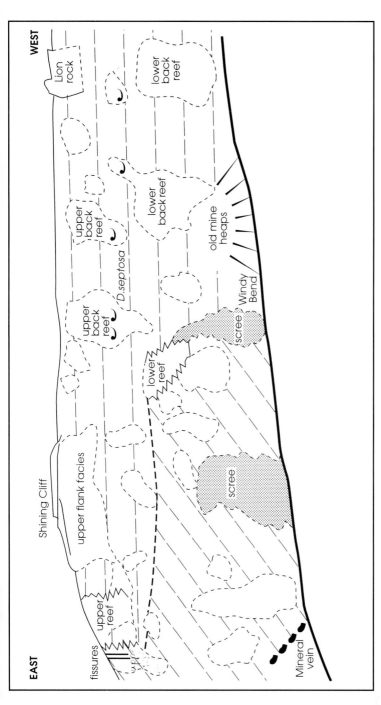

The south side of the Winnats Pass showing the relationships of the reef limestones.

traverses sandstones and shales of the Millstone Grit, with landslips on the north side at Back Tor, Mam Nick and Rushup Edge, overlooking Edale. In both Edale and in the Rushup Valley, the lower slopes are on a sheet of solifluction deposits. Post-glacial streams have cut channels into it.

Cavedale, to the south of Castleton, is a dry valley which shows sections through the reef limestone similar to those in the Winnats Pass. Halfway up the dale is an outcrop of basaltic lava with a few crudely developed columns. The dale lies above parts of Peak Cavern though there is little to show for the cave passages on the surface.

Edale Valley is floored by shales up to about the 325 m contour with sandstones above. Walking uphill there is a distinct steepening of the hill slope at this level. A glance into the deeper stream gulleys shows the contrast from shale to sandstone but often the banks are composed of a shaly sludge with sandstone boulders. This is a solifluction deposit resulting from the movement of partly thawed frozen ground during the waning stages of the Ice Age. Edale is aligned along an anticline or upfold, with the sandstones dipping away on each flank. An early attempt in the search for oil in the core of the anticline was an unsuccessful borehole drilled near the railway bridge at Barber Booth. It reached limestones at over 120 metres but no oil was found.

Kinder Scout is the high plateau to the north of Edale. As the highest ground in the South Pennines it is regarded by some as "The Peak", but it certainly is not peak-shaped! Surrounded by sandstone escarpments the plateau is covered with thick peat deposits, with channels eroded through to the sandstone in places. On the western edge is the waterfall of Kinder Downfall where the stream is often blown back over the top by westerly gales.

Alport Castles, to the northwest of Ladybower Reservoir, is probably the most spectacular landslip, being a mass a kilometre long which has dropped some 50 metres below its parent sandstone cliff on the east side of the dale. The slipped beds are thin sandstones which have weathered into a fantastic array of pinnacles and towers. It is difficult to see how the present small stream could have undermined the escarpment enough to cause its collapse but it was probably much larger in the wetter climate after the Ice Age.

The **Surprise View, Stanage, Millstone, Longshaw, Froggatt, Curbar and Baslow Edges** constitute the long escarpment of the Chatsworth Grit, one of the main deltaic sandstones of the Millstone Grit. Much favoured by rock climbers, the sandstones are coarse and gritty with scattered bands of small pebbles. They were once quarried for making into grindstones for sharpening the knives and tools of the Sheffield steel industry. Both pebbles and sand grains have been derived from the ancient rocks of the Scottish Highlands, and a few pebbles can be matched directly with parent outcrops even after 300 million years. Sometimes long curved partings can be seen in the sandstone cliffs, e.g. at the south end of Stanage Edge above the heap of unfinished millstones - these curved surfaces are sections across the bottoms of river channels on the tops of the delta flats. Occasional gaps in the escarpment are where faults dislocate the strata giving a boost to erosion. On the moors above Hathersage, the two plateaux of Higgar Tor and Carlswark are parts of the same

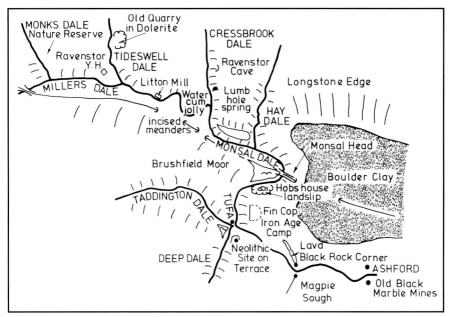

Sketch map of Monsal Dale and Millers Dale.

sandstone bed displaced by faulting. Several of the Edges are capped by isolated gritstone tors with shapes attracting popular names such as "The Coach and Horses".

Axe Edge and the Cat and Fiddle Moors west of Buxton are characterized by sandstone escarpments and widespread peat bogs. On Goldsitch Moss there are the remains of mine shafts sunk to reach a coal seam in the Millstone Grit. To the north the headwaters of the River Goyt flow northwards down a syncline cut in lower Coal Measures, and a few old coal mine adits are still visible.

Ashwood, Chee, Millers and Monsal Dales are parts of the valley of the Derbyshire Wye, draining some 15 km from Buxton to Bakewell. It is the only major river to cross the White Peak entirely on the surface. Parts of its valley are occupied by the A6 road or by the former railway track, now the Monsal Trail. A traverse from west to east shows the anticlinal structure, with limestones dipping west in Ashwood Dale near Buxton, and east in Monsal Dale. The limestone beds of Great Rocks Dale are well exposed below Topley Pike viewpoint and a long series of limestone crags bounds Water-cum-Jolly between Litton and Cressbrook. Interleaved toadstones (lavas) diversify the scenery as can be seen in the Litton cuttings and Knot Low, both above Millers Dale, and again at Black Rock Corner near Ashford-in-the-Water. The impervious volcanic rocks help to keep the river on the surface. The Magpie lead mine sough discharges a stream of water from a tunnel mouth opposite Black Rock Corner. A landslipped mass of cherty limestones forms Hobs House crags in Monsal Dale, famous for its fossil corals. The thin dark limestones near Ashford were once mined to make black marble ornaments of various types, many improved by inlaid coloured marbles.

Sheldon Moor above Monsal Dale has the ruined engine house of **Magpie Mine** (south of Sheldon village) as well as other relics of 19th century lead mining. The shaft eventually reached 720 feet depth. The deepest workings are now flooded but a sough takes away the water at 590 feet.

Lathkill Dale is now mostly a Nature Reserve administered by English Nature. Thick and thin-bedded limestones alternate in its cliffs and there are masses of scree. There are caves in the usually dry upper reaches near Monyash, but the thickly wooded Nature Reserve is on the site of intensive 18th and 19th century lead mining operations. When these ceased in the late 19th century it was an industrial wasteland and now nature has taken over! The pit by the ruined Mandale Engine house once housed a water-wheel 35 feet in diameter, but little can be seen of the larger water-wheel pit at Lathkill Dale Mine. Mandale Sough tail (outfall) is close to the footpath through the dale. The soughs have affected the natural river flow for the last two centuries and the Lathkill is now famous as one of Britain's disappearing rivers. Through parts of its course it only flows on the surface in very wet weather. Its water is rich in dissolved lime and there are tufa deposits at Pudding and Bubble Springs. Lower down, the river bed was puddled with clay to keep water on the surface in the trout stream.

Robin Hood's Stride on Stanton Moor is an isolated remnant of a faulted mass of Millstone Grit. The twin-towered crag is sometimes known as Mock Beggar's Hall from its fancied resemblance to the outline of a stately home.

Alport Heights and Barrel Edge south of Matlock are parts of another deltaic sandstone, whilst **Black Rocks** is a detached landslipped mass. Close to Black Rocks are the disturbed ground and waste heaps of the Old Moor Mines on the Gang Vein, where bits of lead ore, fluorspar, barytes and calcite may easily be found. The nearby High Peak Trail occupies the site of the former Cromford and High Peak Railway, built as an extension to the Cromford Canal in the Derwent Valley below. Far beneath the surface is a series of lead mine drainage soughs, the first having been designed by Sir Cornelius Vermuyden in the 1630s, (Vermuyden was the Dutch engineer responsible for draining the Fens of eastern England). The outflowing water was utilized by Sir Richard Arkwright to power his mill at Cromford, whilst the outflow from Meerbrook Sough near Whatstandwell is still utilized for public water supplies.

North of Black Rocks is a fine view of Cromford and the **Derwent Gorge** near Matlock. The Masson Hill anticline rises on its west flank, whilst to the east is the High Tor reef limestone mass. Several caves and old mines penetrate both sides of the gorge and there is a fine lead-mining museum at Matlock Bath.

Westwards from Black Rocks one is looking along the crest of the Bole Hill anticline, with limestone beds dipping away on the two flanks. To the north is the active Dene Quarry with the beds dipping northwards, whilst to the south is a series of small quarries in the **National Stone Centre** above Wirksworth, with beds dipping southwards. These show instructive sections through reefs and lagoonal limestones adjacent to the High Peak Trail. West of the National Stone Centre, the High Peak Trail crosses The Gulf with shales dropped down between two large faults. West of

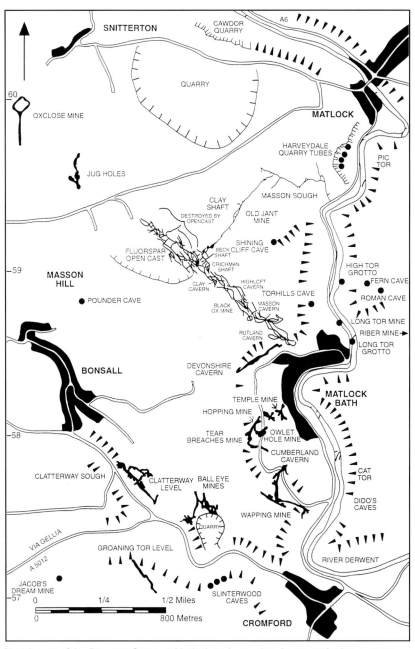

Sketch map of the Derwent Gorge at Matlock and associated cave and mine systems.

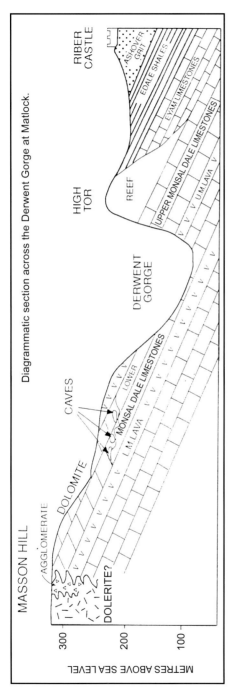

Diagrammatic section across the Derwent Gorge at Matlock.

The Gulf the limestone beds are about 50 m higher than the Stone Centre but a lot has been quarried away in the Middlepeak Quarries. Middleton-by-Wirksworth lies further north along the fault scarp and at Middleton Mine high quality limestone has been mined for the chemical industry from beneath the uplifted block: the workings extend for over a kilometre into the hill.

Harborough Rocks, above Brassington, are crags of dolomitized limestone, containing an archaeological cave. From the Rocks a view may be had of the **Bees Nest and Green Clay** silica-sand pits, containing the partly worked-out sands and clays of the Pliocene Brassington Formation. These are relics of a former sandy and muddy alluvial sheet which subsided into collapse structures in the limestone beneath, to form the Pocket Deposits. Twigs and branches of the fossilized tree *Sequoia* have been found in the clays. Deep below ground northeast of Harborough Rocks are the mine workings and caves of **Golconda Mine** with a warren of passages accessible only to specialists.

Dovedale is in two parts, Upper Dovedale north of Hartington, and Lower Dovedale to the south.

Upper Dovedale is a broad valley where the infant River Dove flows southwards along the boundary between limestones to the east and Millstone Grit to the west. The limestone provides striking scenery with its row of deeply eroded reef masses, Chrome Hill, Parkhouse Hill, High Wheeldon and Wagon Low lying along the western margin of the White Peak. The view from below the hills gives an idea of what a deep sea fish might have seen looking up towards the reefs. Short gorges

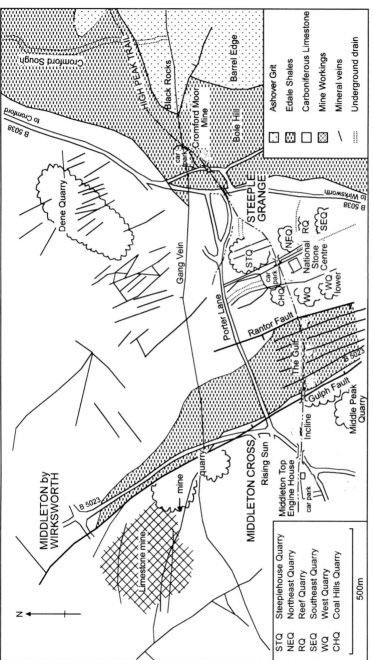

Sketch map of the National Stone Centre and Gulf area, near Wirksworth.

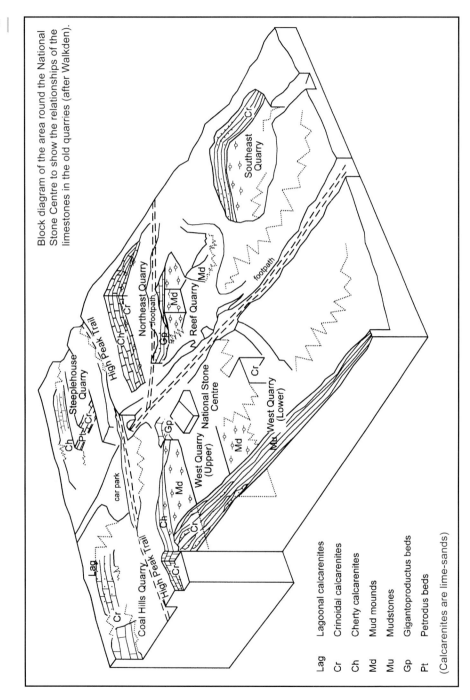

Block diagram of the area round the National Stone Centre to show the relationships of the limestones in the old quarries (after Walkden).

Lag   Lagoonal calcarenites
Cr   Crinoidal calcarenites
Ch   Cherty calcarenites
Md   Mud mounds
Mu   Mudstones
Gp   Gigantoproductus beds
Pt   Petrodus beds

(Calcarenites are lime-sands)

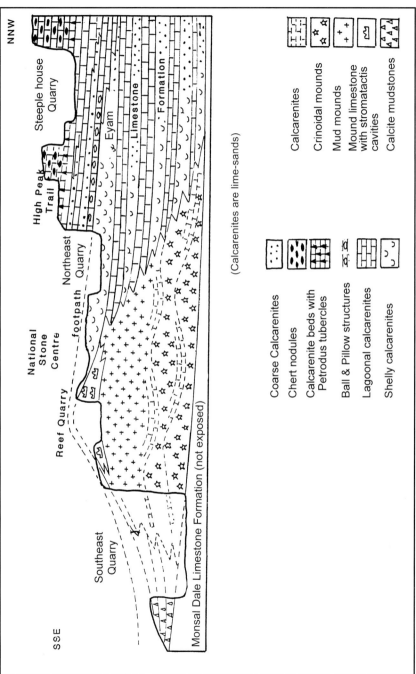

Section through the reef and related limestones at the National Stone Centre (after Walkden).

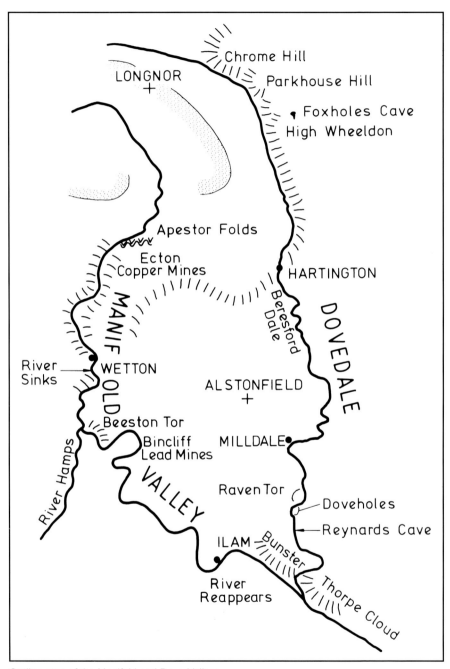

Outline map of the Manifold and Dove Valleys.

between the reefs are smaller equivalents of the Winnats Pass. High Wheeldon has the important archaeological Fox Hole cave near its crest. Finds indicate intermittent human occupation from Neolithic to Roman times, whilst below these a layer of sediment contained bones of bear and other animals from the later part of the Ice Age.

To the west of this stretch of Dovedale is Longnor Edge, the lowest of the Millstone Grit escarpments. Beyond are the jagged ridges of **The Roaches, Hen Cloud and Ramshaw Rocks**, all in the Chatsworth Grit. Tilted up at 45° they lie on either side of the Goyt Syncline, which deepens to the north and contains the lowest strata of the Coal Measures.

Lower Dovedale is the stretch between Hartington and Thorpe. For some 12 km the river winds through a limestone gorge with a succession of different names, Beresford Dale in the north, then Narrowdale, Wolfscote Dale, Mill Dale and finally Dovedale proper. As there is little road access, the dales have retained their natural beauty, though ash woods are more common now and hide some features. There are many small dams across the river to maintain trout fishing pools. Springs, particularly in Mill Dale, more than double its flow in the lower reaches.

The River Dove meanders between a series of reef limestone masses which may be seen in section in the cliffs. Examples are Iron Tors in Wolfscote Dale, Raven Tor in Mill Dale, the Dove Holes Crag, and Tissington Spires. The most impressive reefs are at the southern portal of the dale, Thorpe Cloud on the east and Bunster on the west. Looking up from the car park, the steep slopes are the outer faces of reefs and their crests would have had the waves of the Carboniferous seas breaking there some 310 million years ago. Like the Winnats Pass at Castleton the mouth of Dovedale represents an ancient channel between reefs deepened by more recent erosion.

Reconstructing the palaeo-geography of the Carboniferous sea floor is a matter for geologists studying the details of the limestones. But here anyone with a good imagination can get into his time machine and whisk himself back some 310 million years to find himself in a landscape (or should it be sea-scape?) like a present day Pacific Ocean atoll. Dovedale was on the western margins of a large atoll with deeper water in the Manifold Valley area to the west.

The Carboniferous sea-scape is ancient but Dovedale itself was formed only in the last million years or so. The river meandered over a shale plain at first but as it cut down it exposed the tops of the more resistant limestone reefs, and the river followed the shale-filled hollows between these. Further erosion has cut the whole valley from the limestones.

Although Dovedale is a limestone valley it has few caves. No underground river system is known, though the springs in Mill Dale suggest that there is one in the making. The few high level caves are short and abandoned by any stream. Most have been occupied by animals or humans at some stage.

The Manifold Valley lies to the west of Dovedale but presents many contrasts. Starting on Millstone Grit shales it traverses a limestone gorge from Hulme End to Ilam but the limestones are mostly thin-bedded, dark and with frequent shale partings, typical of sedimentation in deep water. They represent the deep seas flanking the

Derbyshire lagoon and reefs. A few reef-mounds are present in the Manifold Valley, e.g. Beeston Tor, Nan Tor and Thors Cave crag, but they are rather isolated. The thin limestones are exposed in some cuttings on the old railway track, now the Manifold Trail, and in the long-disused quarries at Apes Tor on the north side of Ecton Hill. In the latter they were tightly folded as such beds were less resistant and deformed more easily than reef and lagoonal limestones under the stresses of earth movements. Lagoonal limestones are present in Brownlow Quarry near Waterhouses, now a Nature Reserve.

The Manifold Valley was once the site of an intensive mining industry, mainly copper mines at Ecton and lead mines at Bincliff, as well as lesser mines at Mixon and Royledge to the west. Abandoned over a century ago, some of the mine workings are still accessible at Ecton. Few of the buildings remain, and a lot of the mine workings are below river level and have long been flooded. The lowest workings were some 300 m below river level. The Ecton copper mines were amongst the most spectacular in Europe in the 18th century and the Duke of Devonshire built The Crescent at Buxton out of the profits. Pumping engines were once installed in artificial caverns within the hill. Powered by steam with coal-fired boilers, the smoke went out through old shafts to the summit of the hill, where it gave rise to legends of the Devil inhabiting the nether regions.

The River Manifold is one of Britain's classic disappearing rivers. It normally sinks into its bed near Wetton Mill to re-appear at Ilam some 6 km downstream. But in wet weather the river stays on the surface and sinks at various points down stream, such as Redhurst Swallet and Ladyside Pot, although the latter now seems to be a resurgence, pushing water up to the bed of the river. Both have been explored by cavers in dry weather, but the main stream has not been reached. Only in extremely wet conditions does the river stay on the surface throughout its course. Near Ilam it is joined by springs discharging water from the tributary River Hamps, which also vanishes into its own bed near Waterhouses.

There are several short caves in the Manifold Valley, one with an impressive entrance, Thors Cave. On the hillside above Thors Cave, Elderbush Cave has yielded evidence of both Palaeolithic and Neolithic man, whilst Thors Cave was also used by Romano-British people. Ossom's Eyrie has provided evidence of birds of prey and of the animals on which they lived. A cave at Beeston Tor yielded a hoard of Saxon coins in the 1930s, now in the British Museum.

Like the rest of the Peak District, the Manifold Valley was largely eroded into its present form during the Ice Age, and the last cold phase is represented by the screes at Ecton. Repeated frosts by night and thaws by day shattered the rocks and the fragments accumulated as screes. Later they were partly cemented by percolating rainwater depositing lime. The screes were once quarried for road-building but their crushing strength does not meet modern standards and the gravel pits have long been abandoned.

Aitkenhead, N., Chisholm, J.I., & Stevenson, I.P. 1985. *Geology of the country around Buxton, Leek and Bakewell*. British Geological Survey Memoir, Keyworth, Notts. 168pp.

Chisholm, J.I., Charsley, T. & Aitkenhead, N. 1988. *Geology of the country around Ashbourne and Cheadle*. British Geological Survey Memoir. Keyworth, Notts. 160pp.

Cope, F.W. 1998. *Geology explained in the Peak District*. Scarthin Books, Cromford. 198pp.

Cope, F.W. 1999. *The Peak District*. Geologists Association Guide no. 26, 3rd edition. 78pp.

Dalton, R., Fox, H. & Jones, P. 1988. *Classic Landforms of the White Peak*. Classic Landforms Guide No. 9, Geographical Association, Sheffield. 48pp. (revised edition 1999).

Dalton, R., Fox, H. & Jones, P. 1990. *Classic Landforms of the Dark Peak*. Classic Landforms Guide No. 11, Geographical Association, Sheffield. 48pp. (revised edition 1999).

Ford, T.D. 1963. The Dolomite Tors of Derbyshire. *East Midlands Geographer*, vol.3, no.19, pp.148-153.

Ford, T.D. 1977. *Limestones and Caves of the Peak District*. Geo-Books, Norwich. 469pp.

Ford, T.D. 1986. The Evolution of the Castleton Cave Systems. *Cave Science*, vol. 13, pp.131-148.

Ford, T.D. 1987. The Origin of the Winnats Pass, Castleton. *Mercian Geologist*, vol.10, pp.241-249.

Ford, T.D. 1996. *The Castleton area*. Geologists Association Guide no. 56, 94pp.

Ford, T.D. 1997. The development of the Derwent Gorge and its caves at Matlock, Derbyshire. *Cave & Karst Science*, vol.24, pp. 5-19.

Ford, T.D. 1999. The Growth of Geological Knowledge in the Peak District. *Mercian Geologist*, vol. 14, no.4, pp. 161-190.

Ford, T.D. 2000. *Derbyshire Blue John*. Ashbourne Editions, Ashbourne. 112pp.

Ford, T.D. 2000. Vein cavities: early stages in the evolution of the Castleton cave systems. *Cave & Karst Science*, vol. 27, no.1, pp. 5-14.

Ford, T.D. 2001. The Geology of the Ecton and other northeast Staffordshire mines. *Mining History*, vol. 14, no.4. pp. 1-22

Ford, T.D. & Burek, C.V. 1976. Anomalous Limestone Gorges in Derbyshire. *Mercian Geologist*, vol. 6, pp. 59-66.

Ford, T.D. & Gunn, J. 1990. *Caves & Karst of the Peak District.* British Cave Research Association. Cave Studies Series no.3, 32pp. (second edition 1992).

Ford, T.D., Sarjeant, W.A.S. & Smith, M.E. 1993. Minerals of the Peak District. *Bulletin of the Peak District Mines Historical Society*, vol. 12, no.1, pp. 16-55.

Ford, T.D. & Rieuwerts, J.H (editors). 2000. *Lead Mining in the Peak District*. Landmark Publications, Ashbourne. 208pp.

Harrison, D.J. & Adlam, K.M.McL. 1985. *The limestone and dolomite resources of the Peak District of Derbyshire and Staffordshire*. Mineral Assessment Report of the Institute of Geological Sciences no. 144, 48pp.

Millward, R. & Robinson, A. 1975. *The Peak District*. Eyre Methuen, London. 301pp.

Porter, L. & Robey, J.A. 2000. *The Copper and Lead Mines of North Staffordshire*. Landmark Publications, Ashbourne. 272pp.

Quirk, D.G. 1993. The Origin of the Peak District Orefield. *Bulletin of the Peak District Mines Historical Society,* vol.12, pp.4-15.

Rieuwerts, J.H. 2000. *Lathkill Dale, Derbyshire: its Mines and Miners*. Landmark Publications, Ashbourne. 112pp.

Smith, E.G., Rhys, G.H. & Eden, R.A. 1967. *Geology of the country around Chesterfield, Mansfield and Matlock*. Geological Survey Memoir, 430pp.

Stevenson, I.P. & Gaunt, G. 1971. *Geology of the Country around Chapel-en-le-Frith*. Geological Survey Memoir. 444pp.

Tomlinson, J.M. 1996. *Derbyshire Black Marble*. Peak District Mines Historical Society, Matlock. 96pp.

Waltham, A.C. & Dixon, N. 2000. Movement of the Mam Tor landslide, Derbyshire. *Quarterly Journal of Engineering Geology and Hydrogeology*, vol. 33, pp. 105-123.

Waltham, A.C. & others. 1997. *The Karst and Caves of Great Britain*. Joint Nature Conservation Committee, Peterborough & Chapman & Hall London. 358pp.

Warwick, G.T. 1964. The Dry Valleys of the Southern Pennines. *Erdkunde*, vol.18, pp. 116-123.

Waters, R.S. & Johnson, R.H. 1958. The terraces of the Derbyshire Derwent. *East Midlands Geographer*, vol.2, no.9, pp. 3-15.

Index